Power Maths

Year 5
Practice Book 5A

White Rose Maths edition

Did you use any maths in real life during the summer?

Draw or write what you did.

This book belongs to _____.

My class is _____.

Series editor: Tony Staneff

Lead author: Josh Lury

Consultants (first edition): Professor Liu Jian and Professor Zhang Dan

Author team (first edition): Tony Staneff, Josh Lury, Kate Henshall, Wei Huinv, Steph King, Stephanie Kirk, Timothy Weal and Paul Wrangles

Pearson

Contents

This looks like a good challenge!

It's time to do some practice!

How to use this book

Do you remember how to use this **Practice Book**?

Use the **Textbook** first to learn how to solve this type of problem.

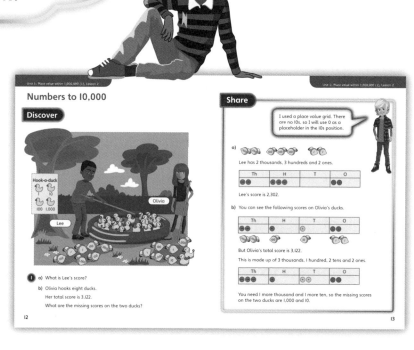

This shows you which **Textbook** page you need.

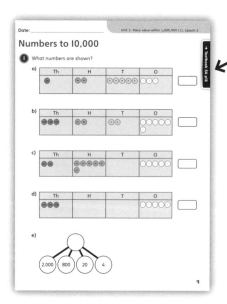

Have a go at questions by yourself using this **Practice Book**. Use what you have learnt.

Challenge questions make you think hard!

Questions with this light bulb make you think differently.

Reflect

Each lesson ends with a Reflect question so you can think about what you have learnt.

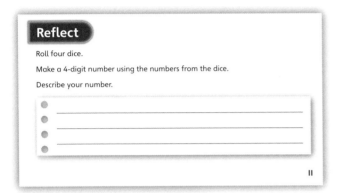

Use My Power Points at the back of this book to keep track of what you have learnt.

My journal

At the end of a unit your teacher will ask you to fill in My journal.

This will help you show how much you can do now that you have finished the unit.

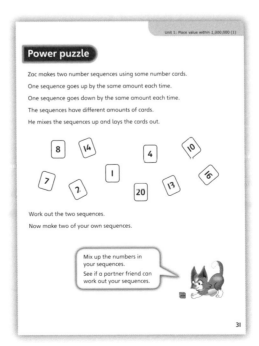

Date: _____

Roman numerals

1 Write these numbers in Roman numerals.

a) 12 ⬚

b) 35 ⬚

c) 43 ⬚

d) 90 ⬚

e) 114 ⬚

Number	Roman numeral
1	I
5	V
10	X
50	L

2 Complete the table to show the multiples of 100 in Roman numerals.

100	C	600	DC
200	CC	700	
300		800	
400		900	
500	D	1,000	M

3 Fill in the missing numbers.

a) MMCXI means  + ⬚ +  + ⬚ +  = ⬚

b) DCCL means  + ⬚ + + ⬚ = ⬚

c) CXCV means + 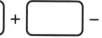 − + = ⬚

6

4 Complete the part-whole models.

a)

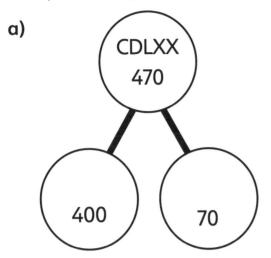

b)

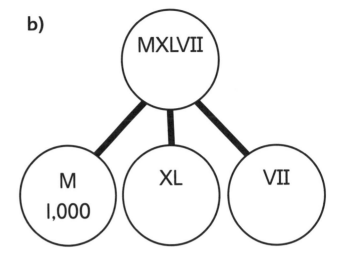

5 a) Draw lines to match each coin with the correct year.

| 1461 | 1211 | 1901 | 1545 |

b) Write the missing Roman numerals on the last coin.

6 Lexi says MCX is the same as CMX because they contain the same letters. Is Lexi correct? Explain your answer.

_____

_____

_____

7 Complete the three sentences using Roman numerals.

a) 10 years earlier than 1985 is ☐ .

b) 100 years later than 1480 is ☐ .

c) 50 years later than 1962 is ☐ .

8 Use each number card once so that the column of numbers below is in descending order.

CHALLENGE

V X L C D

MDC ☐ IX

MC ☐ VI

DCCL ☐

☐ DXXI

CCCX ☐

Think carefully about the size of the number each card represents and which other numerals it can be written before or after.

Reflect

Today, I have learnt that the letter M in Roman numerals represents

_____ . The letter D represents _____ and L represents

_____ .

Together, MDXL represents the number _____ because

_____

_____

Numbers to 10,000

1 What numbers are shown?

a)

Th	H	T	O
1,000	100 100	10 10 10 10 10	1 1 1

b)

Th	H	T	O
1,000 1,000 1,000	100 100	10 10	1 1 1 1 1 1

c)

Th	H	T	O
1,000 1,000	100 100 100 100 100 100		1 1 1 1 1

d)

Th	H	T	O
1,000 1,000 1,000			1 1 1 1 1

e)

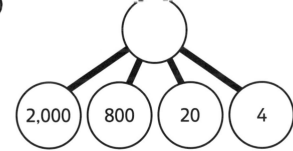

2,000   800   20   4

2 **a)** Draw more place value counters to represent the number 5,632.

Th	H	T	O
1,000 1,000 1,000 1,000	100 100 100	10 10 10	1

b) Fill in the missing numbers.

5,632 = [5,000] + [ ] + [ ] + [ ]

3 What is the value of each underlined digit?

a) 1,7<u>9</u>4 [ ]   **b)** 6,<u>4</u>80 [ ]   **c)** <u>2</u>,058 [ ]

4 What numbers are shown?

a)

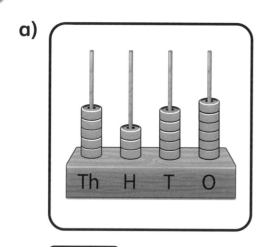

[ ]

c)

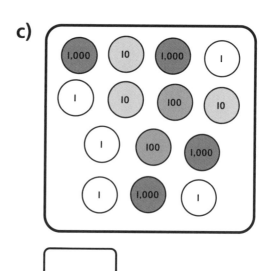

[ ]

b)

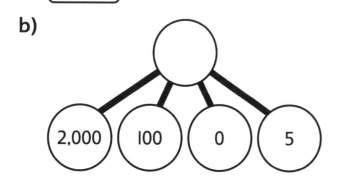

CHALLENGE

5 Here are four digit cards.

| 0 | 2 | 5 | 8 |

I wonder if some of these have more than one answer.

Arrange the digits to make:

a) a number that has 5 hundreds

b) a number that is odd

c) a number where 2 has the value of 20

d) the largest possible even number.

Reflect

Roll four dice.

Make a 4-digit number using the numbers from the dice.

Describe your number.

_____

_____

_____

Date: _____

↑ Textbook 5A p16

Numbers to 100,000

1 **a)** The digit cards represent a 5-digit number.

Write your answers in words.

TTh	Th	H	T	O
8	5	0	1	3

What does the digit 5 represent?   <u>5 thousands</u>

What does the digit 1 represent?   _____

What does the digit 8 represent?   _____

What is the digit in the 100s position?   _____

b) The digit cards 5 and 8 swap positions.

Write the new number in numerals and then in words.

In numerals: [   ]

In words: _____

2 Draw lines to match the value of the digit **4** in each of these four numbers.

43,250	32,409	34,250	23,546

4   40   4,000   40,000   400

3 Draw more counters on the place value grid to show the number 26,415.

TTh	Th	H	T	O
10,000	1,000 1,000 1,000 1,000 1,000	100 100 100 100		1 1 1

4 Complete each part-whole model.

a)

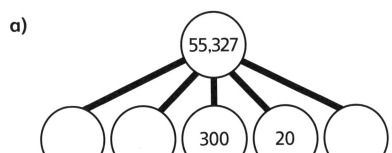

b)

c)

5 a) What is 1,000 more than 13,572? ☐

b) What is 100 more than 13,572? ☐

c) What is 200 less than 13,572? ☐

d) What is 50,000 more than 13,572? ☐

13

6 Max uses these digit cards to make three 5-digit numbers.

| ? | ? | ? | 2 | 0 |

CHALLENGE

His first number is greater than 60,000.

His second number has an even number of hundreds.

His final number has a digit with the value 5,000.

I wonder if any of the digits can be the same.

a) What could the missing digits on the cards be?

[ ] , [ ] and [ ]

b) Which numbers could Max make?

c) Make up your own similar puzzle.

Reflect

Show or write the value of each digit in the number 64,231.

Date: _____

Numbers to 1,000,000

1 How many pencils are there in total?

Write your answer in numerals and words.

    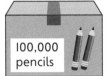

In numerals: there are [ ] pencils in total.

In words: there are _____ pencils in total.

2 What numbers are represented here?

a)

     [ ]

b)

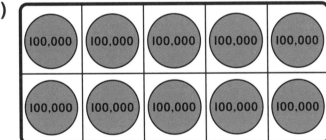 [ ]

c)

HTh	TTh	Th	H	T	O

[ ]

15

3 Bella is watching a video on her computer.

Write the number of views in words.

123,419 views

_____

_____

_____

4 Draw the number 126,300 in the place value grid.

HTh	TTh	Th	H	T	O

5 Write each of the following numbers in numerals.

a) Three hundred and twenty-nine thousand and one hundred.

b) Six hundred thousand and forty.

c)

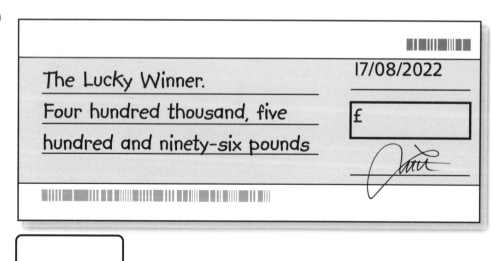

6 What does the 4 represent in each of these numbers?

a) 314,912 _____

b) 240 _____

c) 500,240 _____

d) 77,314 _____

e) Four hundred and eight thousand, three hundred and one.

_____

7 Olivia makes this number.

CHALLENGE

HTh	TTh	Th	H	T	O
●●●	●		●	●●	●●●●●

Olivia moves two counters. Her number now has 1 thousand.

What could the new number be? Find five possible answers.

[ ] , [ ] , [ ] , [ ] , [ ]

Reflect

Write a 6-digit number. [ ]

Swap the number with a partner.

Say the number aloud and write it in words.

- _____
- _____
- _____

Date: _____

Read and write 5- and 6-digit numbers

→ Textbook 5A p24

1 Each dice is one digit of a number.

Write each number correctly, including a comma.

a)

_____

b)

_____

c)

_____

d)

_____

2 Arrange the digit cards to make 6-digit numbers.

Use each card once for each number.

Write the numbers you find.

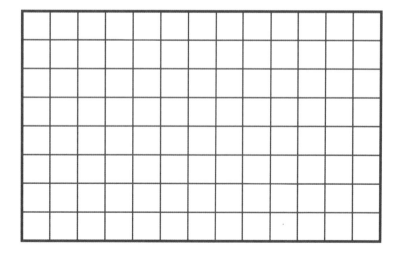

I will try to find all the possible numbers.

18

3 Match the number pairs.

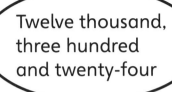

Twelve thousand, three hundred and twenty-four

TTh	Th	H	T	O
3	0	1	0	3

Twelve thousand and twenty-five

TTh	Th	H	T	O
1	2	0	2	5

Thirteen thousand, one hundred and thirty

TTh	Th	H	T	O
1	3	1	3	0

Thirty thousand, one hundred and three

TTh	Th	H	T	O
1	2	3	2	4

4 Re-write each 4-, 5- or 6-digit number so the comma is in the correct place.

32,15 $\longrightarrow$ _____   2,1215 $\longrightarrow$ _____

203,21 $\longrightarrow$ _____   107,3 $\longrightarrow$ _____

42,3471 $\longrightarrow$ _____   5,08017 $\longrightarrow$ _____

1,9999 $\longrightarrow$ _____   90,9909 $\longrightarrow$ _____

5 Here is a mystery 5-digit number.

 × × = 0

 × = 10

 × × = 40

 + =

 × = 4

What is the mystery number?

Reflect

What could this number be? Did you write the same number as a partner?

Powers of 10

1 How many hundreds in each number?

a) 1,400 = ☐ hundreds

Th	H	T	O
1,000	100 100 100 100		

b) 2,500 = ☐ hundreds

Th	H	T	O
1,000 1,000	100 100 100 100 100		

c) 9,700 = ☐ hundreds

d) 12,000 = ☐ hundreds

2 Complete the sentences.

a) 31,000 = ☐ thousands

b) 73,000 = ☐ thousands

c) 126,000 = ☐ thousands

21

3 Max has made the number 5,000.

Th	H	T	O
1,000 1,000 1,000 1,000 1,000			

a) He exchanges each 1,000 counter for ten 100s.

How many 100 counters does he have? ☐

b) He now exchanges each 100 counter for ten 10s.

How many 10 counters does he have? ☐

c) He now exchanges each 10 counter for ten 1s.

How many 1 counters does he have? ☐

4 Complete the sentences.

a) 24,000 = ☐ thousands

24,000 = ☐ hundreds

24,000 = ☐ tens

b) 213,000 = ☐ thousands

213,000 = ☐ hundreds

213,000 = ☐ tens

5 A number is made up of 23 hundreds.

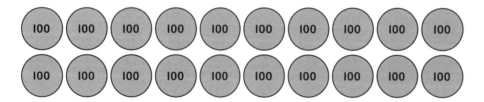

What is the number? ☐

6

1,000,000

CHALLENGE

Complete the sentences.

One million = [ ] hundred thousands

One million = [ ] ten thousands

One million = [ ] thousands

One million = [ ] hundreds

One million = [ ] tens

One million = [ ] ones

Reflect

Complete this sequence.

3, 30, 300, [ ], [ ], [ ]

Describe the pattern that you notice.

_____

_____

_____

_____

Date: _____

10/100/1,000/10,000/100,000 more or less

1 Bella makes a number on a place value grid.

HTh	TTh	Th	H	T	O
●●	●●●		●●●●	●	●●●●● ●

a) What number has Bella made?

b) What is 10,000 more than Bella's number?

c) Bella adds one 100 counter to the place value grid.

What number has Bella made now?

d) Bella removes one 10,000 counter from the
place value grid.

What number does Bella have now?

2 Complete these sequences.

a) 140,000 , 150,000 , 160,000 , [ ] , [ ] ,

[ ] , [ ] ,

b) 96,000 , [ ] , 98,000 , 99,000 , [ ] ,

[ ] , [ ] ,

c) [ ] , 760,500 , 760,600 , [ ] , [ ] ,

760,900 , [ ]

24

3 Complete the table for the number 795,104.

100,000 less		100,000 more	
10,000 less		10,000 more	
1,000 less		1,000 more	
100 less		100 more	
10 less		10 more	

4 Complete the following sentences.

a) 100,000 more than 777,777 is ☐.

b) 10,000 less than 444,444 is ☐.

c) 1,000 more than 555,555 is ☐.

5 Complete these sequences.

a) 108,150, 208,150, ☐, ☐, ☐, 608,150, ☐

b) 535,420, 545,420, ☐, ☐, ☐, ☐

c) 751,087, ☐, ☐, 751,117, ☐, ☐

6 Complete the sequence in three ways.

☐, ☐, ☐, ☐, 720,000, ☐

☐, ☐, ☐, ☐, 720,000, ☐

☐, ☐, ☐, ☐, 720,000, ☐

7 Complete the following sentences.

a) 100,000 more than 725,007 is [   ] .

b) 10,000 more than 174,512 is [   ] .

c) 1,000 less than 870,300 is [   ] .

d) [   ] is 10,000 more than 372,150.

e) 492,107 is 100,000 more than [   ] .

f) 183,512 is 1,000 less than [   ] .

8 Here is some information about three number cards, labelled A, B and C.

CHALLENGE

- A is 100,000 more than B.
- C is 10,000 more than B.
- C is 1,000 less than 37,928.

Use all of the information to work out the values of A, B and C.

A = [   ]   B = [   ]   C = [   ]

Reflect

Will it take longer to count in 100s from 100,000 to 200,000 or to count in 10,000s? Explain your answer.

_____

_____

_____

Partition numbers to 1,000,000

1 How many counters are there?

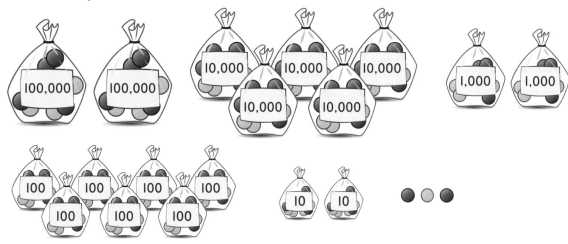

There are [ ] counters.

2 How much money is shown?

There is £ [ ] shown.

3 What number is shown?

HTh	TTh	Th	H	T	O
●	●●●●●● ●	●●●●● ●●●		●●●	●●

[ ]

27

4 Write the value of the underlined digit.

a) 76,128 □

b) 610,950 □

c) 7,318 □

5 Complete the partitions and fill in the missing numbers below.

a) 218,492 = 200,000 + □0,000 + □,000 + □00 + □0 + □

b) 710,388 = □00,000 + □ + □ + □ + □

c) 39,448 = □ + □ + □ + □ + □

d) 200,000 + 70,000 + 9,000 + 700 + 30 + 1 = □

e) 500,000 + 2,000 + 900 + 80 + 1 = □

f) 7,000 + 70 + 3 = □

g) 600,000 + 50,000 + 100 + 3 = □

6 What are these partitioned numbers?

a) 5 hundred thousands, 4 ten thousands, 9 thousands, 5 hundreds,

2 tens and 7 ones [ ]

b) 7 ten thousands, 5 hundreds and 6 ones [ ]

c) 9 hundred thousands, 1 ten thousand, 2 tens and 8 ones [ ]

7 Work out the missing numbers.

a) 28,230 – 8,000 = [ ]

28,230 – 200 = [ ]

28,230 – 30 = [ ]

b) 615,804 – [ ] = 605,804

615,804 – [ ] = 615,004

615,804 – [ ] = 600,000

Reflect

Write down two 5-digit numbers and two 6-digit numbers with 4 as the hundreds digit for each. How did you work out your answers?

- _____
- _____
- _____

Date: _____

End of unit check

My journal

→ Textbook 5A p40

1 Describe the number 12,546 using as many keywords as you can.

Represent and draw it in different ways.

_____

_____

_____

_____

_____

_____

_____

_____

Keywords:

partition, more, less, closer to, half-way, multiple, round

Power check

How do you feel about your work in this unit?

Power puzzle

Zac makes two number sequences using some number cards.

One sequence goes up by the same amount each time.

One sequence goes down by the same amount each time.

The sequences have different amounts of cards.

He mixes the sequences up and lays the cards out.

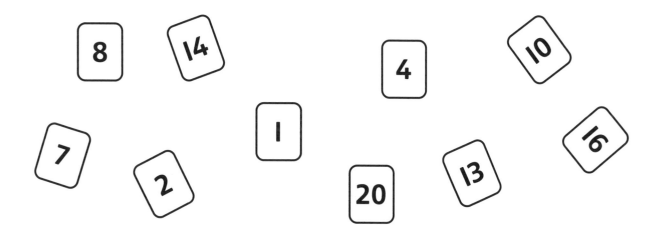

Work out the two sequences.

Now make two of your own sequences.

Mix up the numbers in your sequences.

See if a partner friend can work out your sequences.

Date: _____

Number line to 1,000,000

1 What number is each of the arrows pointing to?

a)

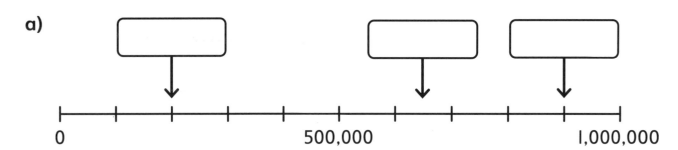

0   500,000   1,000,000

b)

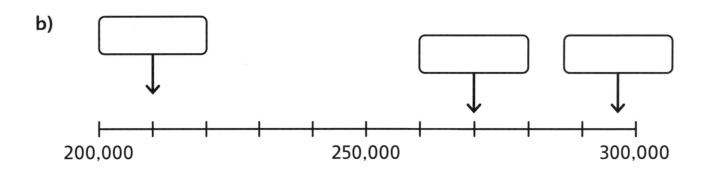

200,000   250,000   300,000

c)

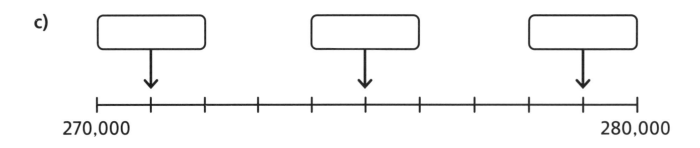

270,000   280,000

d)

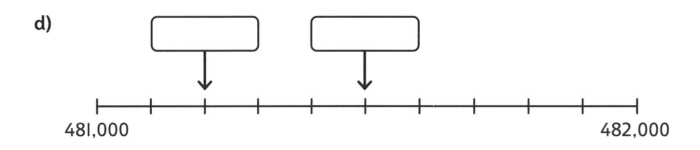

481,000   482,000

2 Draw an arrow from each number to its correct position on the number line.

a)

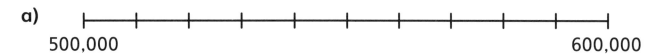

500,000   600,000

525,000   570,000   599,000

b)

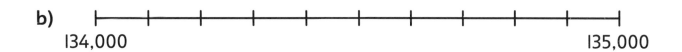

134,000   135,000

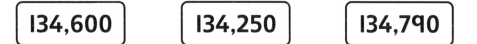

134,600   134,250   134,790

c)

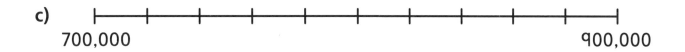

700,000   900,000

800,000   740,000   870,000

3 Estimate the following values for points A, B and C.

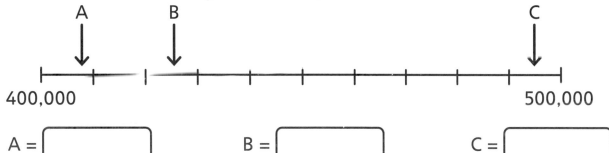

A = [ ]   B = [ ]   C = [ ]

Discuss your method with a partner.

4. Circle all of the numbers that lie between points A and B.

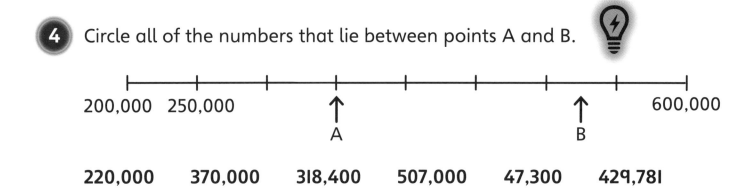

220,000   370,000   318,400   507,000   47,300   429,781

5. A number is marked on the top number line.

Mark the same number on each of the other two number lines.

CHALLENGE

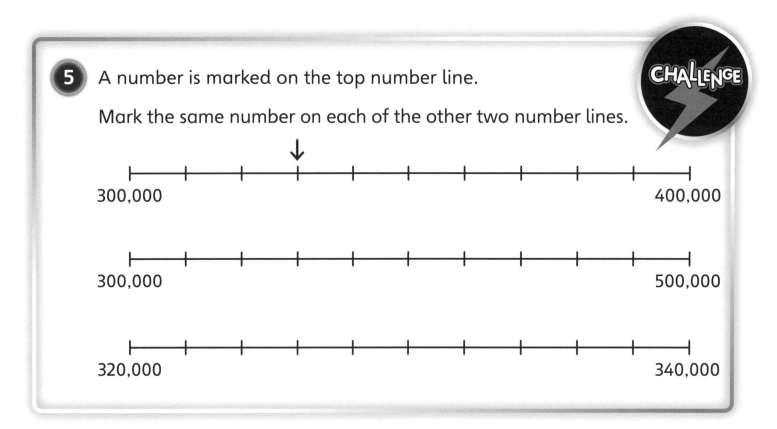

Reflect

Divide the number line up into equal intervals.

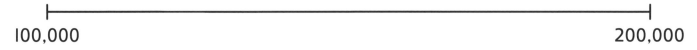

100,000   200,000

Mark 175,000 and 190,000 on the number line.

Discuss with your partner how you worked out how to divide the number line into intervals.

Compare and order numbers to 100,000

→ Textbook 5A p48

1 Compare the two numbers on the place value grid.

TTh	Th	H	T	O
10,000 10,000 10,000 10,000 10,000 10,000 10,000 10,000	1,000 1,000 1,000 1,000		10 10 10 10	1 1 1 1 1 1

TTh	Th	H	T	O
10,000 10,000 10,000 10,000 10,000 10,000 10,000 10,000	1,000 1,000 1,000 1,000		10 10 10 10 10	1 1 1 1

Which is greater? Explain why.

_____

_____

2 Circle the greater number in each group.

a) 17,118   23,900

b) 46,000   40,700

c) 30,095   7,652

d) 45,000   43,200

3 Compare the numbers using less than (<) or greater than (>).

a) 25,118 ◯ 26,300

b) 5,980 ◯ 5,874

c) 48,050 ◯ 95,300

d) 918 ◯ 80,000

4 Write the numbers in order.

Start with the smallest number.

TTh	Th	H	T	O
2	3	4	6	0
3	2	6	0	4
	6	4	3	2
2	6	0	3	4

Smallest   Greatest

5 Write these numbers in ascending order.

63,124	54,500	6,395	51,795

6 Which statements are true? Circle your answers.

a) | 5,287 | 52,872 | 52,782 |

The numbers are written in ascending order.   True / False

b) | 98,275 | 98,257 | 89,625 | 9,865 |

The numbers are written in descending order.   True / False

7 Order these distances from longest to shortest.

11,651 km   11,561 km   9,999 km   13,320 km   13,200 km

[ ]   [ ]   [ ]   [ ]   [ ]

8 Use all of the digit cards 9, 7, 6 and 7 to make the statement correct.

| 9 | 7 | 6 | 7 |

5[ ],[ ]87 < 56,[ ][ ]4

CHALLENGE

9 Car A costs more than Car B.

The digits 0, 1, 2, 4 and 5 appear in both prices.

Find five different pairs of prices.

Write your solutions in the table below.

Car A					
Car B					

Reflect

True or false? 9,623 is greater than 12,345 because it starts with a greater digit.

Explain your answer to a partner.

Date: _____

Compare and order numbers to 1,000,000

1 Tick the greater number.

HTh	TTh	Th	H	T	O
(100,000) (100,000)	(10,000) (10,000) (10,000) (10,000) (10,000)	(1,000) (1,000) (1,000) (1,000) (1,000) (1,000)	(100) (100)	(10) (10) (10) (10) (10) (10) (10) (10)	(1) (1)

The number is [＿＿＿＿]. It is greater [ ].

HTh	TTh	Th	H	T	O
(100,000) (100,000)	(10,000) (10,000) (10,000) (10,000) (10,000)	(1,000) (1,000) (1,000) (1,000) (1,000) (1,000) (1,000) (1,000)	(100) (100) (100)		

The number is [＿＿＿＿]. It is greater [ ].

2 Circle the greater number in each group.

a) 381,402   700,000

b) 280,000   275,300

c) 518,000   six hundred thousand

d) 52,300   523,000

3 Complete the following number sentences using the signs < or >.

a) 56,720 ◯ 73,405

b) 300,000 ◯ 37,940

c) 517,182 ◯ 517,185

d) 59,472 ◯ 59,505

e) one million ◯ 764,914

f) 3,189 ◯ thirty thousand

4 Complete the table by putting the following three populations in descending order.

City	Population
Stirling	31,200
Sunderland	265,180
Swansea	238,700

City	Population

5 The number of litres of milk produced on four farms is shown in the place value table.

	100,000s	10,000s	1,000s	100s	10s	1s
Shaw Farm	3	1	8	0	2	5
Fred's Farm	2	7	4	3	1	3
Croft Top	3	1	8	0	4	0
Cliff Edge		7	2	4	8	1

a) Which farm produced the smallest amount of milk?

_____

b) Now put the four farms in order of how much milk they produced, starting with the farm that produced the smallest amount of milk.

_____

_____

39

6 **a)** Write the following numbers in ascending order.

183,000   289,400   180,500   76,500

_____

b) Write the following numbers in descending order.

195,317   1,000,000   728,905   724,300

_____

7 Make each of these number sentences correct by adding the missing digits.

a) ⑤⑥①,⬜③⑤ < ⑤⑥①,④⑧②

b) ⑥⑤,⑨⬜⑧ > ⑥⬜,⑨③⑥

c) ④⬜⑤,③⬜⑧ > ④⑦⬜,③⬜⑧

d) ①⑧,②⬜⑦ = ①⬜,②⬜⑦

e) ②①⑦,⑨⬜⬜① < ⬜①⑤,⬜⑧⑧

Reflect

What would you do first to compare two 6-digit numbers?

First I would _____

_____

_____

Round numbers to the nearest 100,000

1 Write three different numbers for each shaded section of the number line.

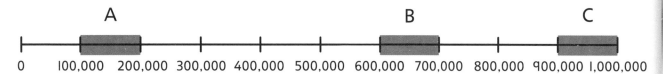

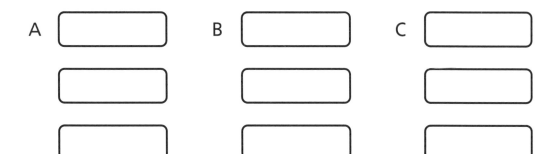

A [   ]   B [   ]   C [   ]

[   ]   [   ]   [   ]

[   ]   [   ]   [   ]

2 Label the half-way numbers on the number lines.

a)

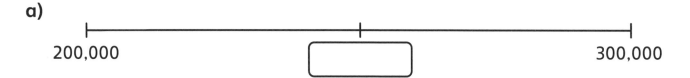

200,000 [   ] 300,000

b)

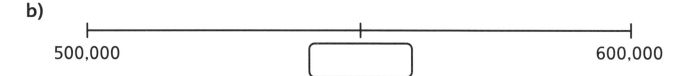

500,000 [   ] 600,000

c)

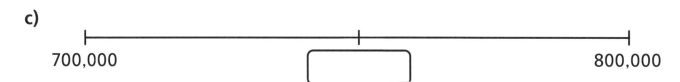

700,000 [   ] 800,000

d)

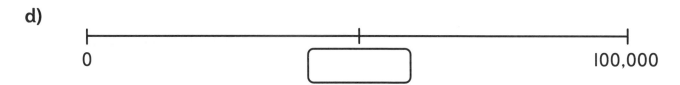

0 [   ] 100,000

3 Complete the previous and next 100,000.

Previous 100,000		Next 100,000
	225,623	
	594,088	
	851,000	
	901,110	
	57,318	

4 Round each number to the nearest 100,000.

a) 225,623 rounds to [ ]

b) 594,088 rounds to [ ]

c) 851,000 rounds to [ ]

d) 901,110 rounds to [ ]

e) 57,318 rounds to [ ]

f) 357,000 rounds to [ ]

g) 800,050 rounds to [ ]

h) 45,000 rounds to [ ]

i) 999,049 rounds to [ ]

j) 300,000 rounds to [ ]

5 Arrange the six digit cards to make two numbers that make each statement true.

CHALLENGE

| 0 | 0 | 2 | 4 | 6 | 8 |

[   ] and [   ] round to 900,000

[   ] and [   ] round to 800,000

[   ] and [   ] round to 700,000

[   ] and [   ] round to 600,000

[   ] and [   ] round to 500,000

[   ] and [   ] round to 400,000

[   ] and [   ] round to 300,000

[   ] and [   ] round to 200,000

Reflect

What method do you use to round a 6-digit number to the nearest 100,000?

What mistakes could someone make?

_____

_____

_____

Date: _____

Round numbers to the nearest 10,000

1) Write three different numbers from each shaded section of the number line.

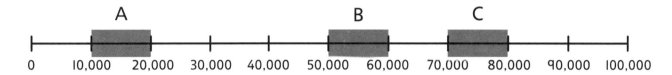

A ⬚

B ⬚

C ⬚

A ⬚

B ⬚

C ⬚

A ⬚

B ⬚

C ⬚

2) Label the half-way numbers on the number lines.

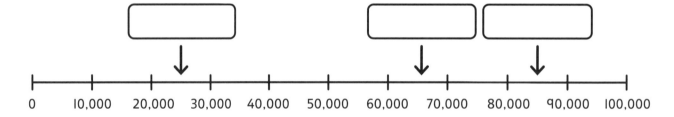

3) Label the half-way numbers on the number lines.

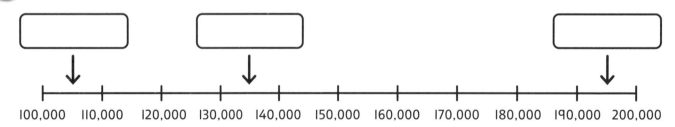

3 Complete the previous and next 10,000.

Previous 10,000		Next 10,000
	25,623	
	74,088	
	81,000	
	6,110	
	98,318	

4 Round each number to the nearest 10,000.

a) 145,107 rounds to [　　　]

b) 245,107 rounds to [　　　]

c) 445,107 rounds to [　　　]

d) 545,107 rounds to [　　　]

e) 645,107 rounds to [　　　]

f) 851,496 rounds to [　　　]

g) 853,496 rounds to [　　　]

h) 855,496 rounds to [　　　]

i) 857,496 rounds to [　　　]

j) 859,496 rounds to [　　　]

CHALLENGE

6 Complete these sentences and draw diagrams to show your ideas.

a) When rounding to the nearest 10,000, you round to 10,000 if...

_____

_____

b) When rounding to the nearest 10,000, you round to 0 if...

_____

_____

c) When rounding to the nearest 10,000, you round to 1,000,000 if...

_____

_____

_____

Reflect

Write six different numbers that round to 70,000 to the nearest 10,000. Try to find numbers no one else in your class thought of.

_____

_____

_____

Round numbers to the nearest 10, 100 and 1,000

↱ Textbook 5A p64

1 Round this number...

100,000s	10,000s	1,000s	100s	10s	1s
3	9	1	6	2	4

to the nearest 100,000 [ ]

to the nearest 10,000 [ ]

to the nearest 1,000 [ ]

to the nearest 100 [ ]

to the nearest 10 [ ]

2 The table below shows the money raised for two charities.

Complete the table.

	Amount raised	Rounded to the nearest £10	Rounded to the nearest £100	Rounded to the nearest £1,000
Charity A	£4,704			£5,000
Charity B	£5,345		£5,300	

3 Complete the table for the numbers shown.

Number	Rounded to the nearest 10,000 it is:	Rounded to the nearest 1,000 it is:	Rounded to the nearest 100 it is:	Rounded to the nearest 10 it is:
96,304				
8,195				
138,057				

4 What is the minimum and maximum each mass could be?

Each mass has been rounded to the nearest 100 kg.

a)

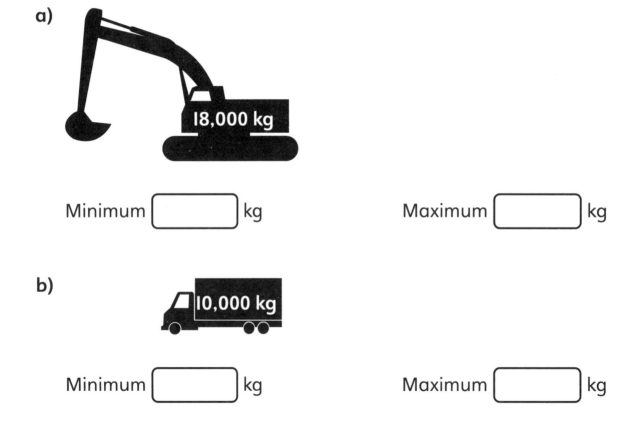

18,000 kg

Minimum [   ] kg   Maximum [   ] kg

b)

10,000 kg

Minimum [   ] kg   Maximum [   ] kg

5 Zac's number is 555,999.

Complete the table to show how his number rounds up.

Number	Nearest 100,000	Nearest 10,000	Nearest 1,000	Nearest 100	Nearest 10
555,999					

6 Sara thinks of a 5-digit number.

- Her number rounds up to the next 10,000.

- It rounds down to the nearest 1,000.

- It rounds down to the nearest 100.

- It rounds up to the nearest 10.

Write down three 5-digit numbers that Sara could be thinking about.

Reflect

Olivia is thinking of a 6-digit number.

When I round my number to the nearest 100,000, all of the digits change.

What could Olivia's number be? | |

Date: _____

End of unit check

My journal

→ Textbook 5A p68

 ①

| 1 | 3 | 5 | 6 | 8 | 9 |

Look at the six digit cards. Use all of the digit cards each time to make the following:

A number between 250,000 and 350,000.	
A number that has a smaller number of 100s than 10,000s.	
The greatest even number that can be made.	
A number that rounds to 600,000 to the nearest 100,000.	
The smallest number that rounds to 600,000 to the nearest 100,000.	
The number that is 10,000 less than 875,913.	

Find more than one answer if you can.

Power check

How do you feel about your work in this unit?   ?

Power play

You will need: 1–6 numbered dice, a set of coloured counters for each player

The aim: To make a row, column or diagonal with four of your counters to win.

Take it in turns to tick a numbered square and then roll the dice to find out what task needs to be done to the ticked number. Then do the task and give the answer.

A player puts their counter on the square if their partner agrees the answer is correct. If not, no counter is placed and the next player takes their turn.

123,650	6,423	54,934	65,347	8,200	19,576
84,547	8,454	45,934	65,437	820,000	91,756
42,702	248,333	88,231	15,656	3,999	39,909
45,207	54,207	88,321	49,783	9,399	40,000
100,000	5,420	45,420	4,978	99,349	99,439
1,499	14,990	12,402	21,402	24,240	529,934

If you roll:	
1	Say the number that is 1,000 more.
2	Round the number to the nearest 10,000.
3	Compare the number with a number in a neighbouring square. Is it larger or smaller?
4	Say the two multiples of 1,000 that the number sits between.
5	Round the number to the nearest 100.
6	Say the value of the first digit in the number.

Try using a 1–9 dice or spinner for the game. Create actions to be carried out for the numbers 7, 8 and 9. Challenge yourself!

Date: _____

Mental strategies (addition)

1 Work out

a)

$2 + 6 = \boxed{}$

$20 + 60 = \boxed{}$

$200 + 600 = \boxed{}$

$2{,}000 + 6{,}000 = \boxed{}$

$20{,}000 + 60{,}000 = \boxed{}$

b)

$7 + 5 = \boxed{}$

$70 + 50 = \boxed{}$

$700 + 500 = \boxed{}$

$7{,}000 + 5{,}000 = \boxed{}$

2 Work out

a) $300 + 600 = \boxed{}$

b) $2{,}000 + 4{,}000 = \boxed{}$

c) $40{,}000 + 40{,}000 = \boxed{}$

d) $300{,}000 + 400{,}000 = \boxed{}$

3 Emma is working out these calculations in her head.

Fill in the thought bubbles to show the steps she might take.

a) 62 + 35

b) 150 + 170

4 Work out mentally the answers to these groups of calculations.

a)

26 + 31 = ☐

31 + 26 = ☐

260 + 310 = ☐

2,600 + 3,100 = ☐

c)

72 + 15 = ☐

15 + 72 = ☐

150 + 720 = ☐

72,000 + 15,000 = ☐

b)

281 + 7 = ☐

7 + 281 = ☐

7 + 1,281 = ☐

7 + 2,810 = ☐

d)

720 + 120 = ☐

120 + 720 = ☐

12,000 + 72,000 = ☐

7,200 + 1,200 = ☐

5 Fill in the thought bubbles to show how you can work out each of these calculations in your head.

a) 64 + 83

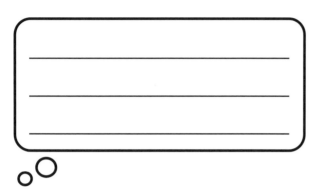

c) 53 + 553

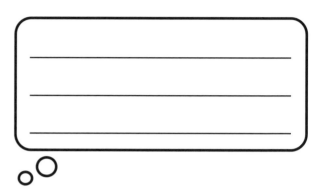

b) 260 + 197

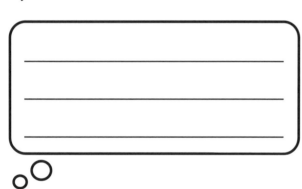

d) 199 + 199

6 Solve these problems mentally.

a) 340 + 890 = ☐

b) 38 + 41 + 199 = ☐

CHALLENGE

Reflect

Discuss with a partner how you can work out each of these calculations in your head.

45 + 32

450 + 380

360 + 198

Mental strategies (subtraction)

→ Textbook 5A p76

 a) Complete these two mental methods for working out 78 – 25.

78 – 20 = ☐

☐ – 5 = ☐

So, 78 – 25 = ☐

70 – 20 = ☐

8 – 5 = ☐

So, 78 – 25 = ☐

b) Complete these two mental methods for working out 670 – 220.

670 – 200 = ☐

☐ – 20 = ☐

So, 670 – 220 = ☐

600 – 200 = ☐

70 – 20 = ☐

So, 670 – 220 = ☐

2 Solve these calculations mentally.

a) 64 – 21 = ☐

b) 640 – 210 = ☐

c) 6,400 – 2,100 = ☐

d) 78 – 41 = ☐

e) 560 – 260 = ☐

f) 97 – 75 = ☐

g) 970 – 750 = ☐

h) 9,700 – 7,500 = ☐

i) 390 – 140 = ☐

j) 6,600 – 3,400 = ☐

3 Jamie is trying to work out the answer to this calculation in her head.

85 – 37

I then subtract 5 to take me to the next 10.

First I subtract 30.

I now subtract 2 more.

a) Complete the calculation Jamie has done in her head.

85 – 30 = ☐

☐ – 5 = ☐

☐ – 2 = ☐

So, 85 – 37 = ☐

b) Show Jamie's method on the number line below.

85

4 Work out these calculations mentally.

a) 45 – 18 = ☐

72 – 45 = ☐

b) 196 – 74 = ☐

196 – 78 = ☐

c) 52 – 36 = ☐

92 – 39 = ☐

d) 144 – 62 = ☐

144 – 66 = ☐

5 Solve these calculations in your head.

a) $192 - 188 = \boxed{}$

b) $304 - 296 = \boxed{}$

c) $347 - 339 = \boxed{}$

d) $102 - 89 = \boxed{}$

e) $401 - 391 = \boxed{}$

f) $1{,}200 - 1{,}184 = \boxed{}$

g) The difference between 8,002 and 7,997 is $\boxed{}$.

6 Solve these problems mentally.

a) $324 - 63 = \boxed{}$

b) 83 subtracted from $830 = \boxed{}$

c) $126 + 75 - 194 = \boxed{}$

d) $425 - 37 = \boxed{}$

e) $126 - 75 + 194 = \boxed{}$

Reflect

Subtract 792 from 801 in your head.

Explain to a partner how you did it, and why you did it like this.

Date: _____

Add whole numbers with more than 4 digits ❶

1 Work out the following additions.

a)

TTh	Th	H	T	O
●●●	●●●●●● ●	●●●●●	●●●●●●	●●●●●● ●●●●
	●●	●●●●●● ●●●● ●●		

	TTh	Th	H	T	O	
		3	6	4	5	9	
+			2	9	2	0	

b)

	TTh	Th	H	T	O	
		1	8	7	2	4	
+		2	4	1	0	0	

d)

	TTh	Th	H	T	O	
		3	9	1	7	5	
+		4	2	3	3	4	

c)

	TTh	Th	H	T	O	
			5	7	8	8	
+		7	2	0	0	8	

e)

	TTh	Th	H	T	O	
		1	5	2	6	1	
+				9	8	4	

2 Kate works out 53,175 + 4,362.

a) What mistake has Kate made?

_____

_____

		TTh	Th	H	T	O
		5	3	1	7	5
	+	4	3	6	2	
		9	6	7	9	5

b) What is the correct answer to the addition?

		TTh	Th	H	T	O
	+					

3 Solve the following calculations.

a) 17,270 + 24,195

b) 45,907 + 33,284

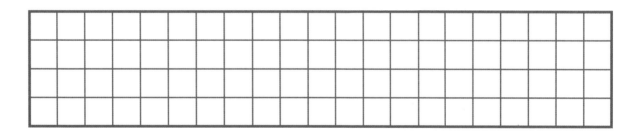

4 Work out the missing digits.

a)

		TTh	Th	H	T	O	
			3			1	0
	+		2	6	1		
				1	6	4	8

b)

		TTh	Th	H	T	O	
			7	3	8	2	
	+				3	9	5
			7	8			0

5 What is ...

    a) five more than four hundred thousand? [ ]

    b) fifty more than four hundred thousand? [ ]

    c) five thousand more than four hundred thousand? [ ]

    d) five thousand more than forty thousand? [ ]

6 Isla plays a computer game.

CHALLENGE

On the first level she gets 26,500 points.

On the second level she gets 2,300 more points than the first level.

How many points does she score in total?

Reflect

Explain to a partner how to work out 42,380 + 29,526. Explain the steps that they should use.

Add whole numbers with more than 4 digits ❷

→ Textbook 5A p84

1 Solve these calculations. They will involve more than one exchange.

a)

		TTh	Th	H	T	O	
		1	6	4	0	4	
	+	2	7	3	4	9	

c)

		TTh	Th	H	T	O	
			4	8	5	7	5
	+		3	2	3	2	8

b)

		TTh	Th	H	T	O	
		1	7	1	7	2	
	+	2	7	3	5	5	

2 Solve the following calculations.

a) 127,420 + 337,293

b) 37,915 + 8,759

c) 11,759 + 817

d) 519,000 + 294,000

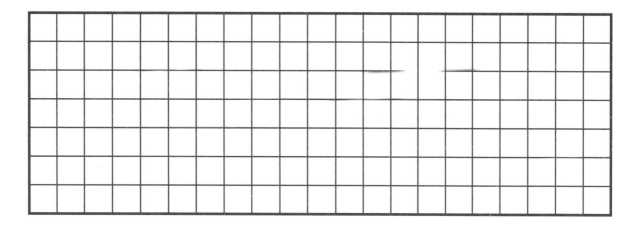

3 Three children are swimming for charity. Alex swims 1,925 metres, Lexi swims 2,150 metres and Olivia swims 2,475 metres.

a) They have to swim at least 6,000 metres in total. Have they reached their target? Show all your working.

b) How do you know the total will be a multiple of 10 before you even add the numbers together?

_____

_____

4 Max is working out 26,348 + 6,293.

a) What mistake has Max made?

_____

_____

_____

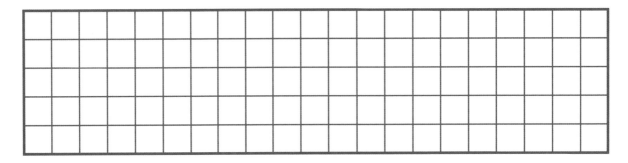

	TTh	Th	H	T	O
		2	6	3	4	8
+		6	2	9	3	
		8	9	2	7	8

b) What is the correct answer? Draw your own column addition.

5 Fill in the missing digits.

a)

	TTh	Th	H	T	O	
	2	5	7	8		
+		6	2		1	
	6			1	5	

b)

	Hth	TTh	Th	H	T	O	
			5		4	2	6
+	3	1	3			2	4
		9		0	0		

6 Use the digits on the cards to make the additions correct.
Use each digit card once in each addition.

0	1	2	3	4	5	6	7	8	9

a)

	TTh	Th	H	T	O	
+						
	9	9	6	5	7	

b)

	TTh	Th	H	T	O	
+						
	9	0	0	0	0	

Reflect

Write an addition with two 5-digit numbers that has exactly two exchanges.

Date: _____

Subtract whole numbers with more than 4 digits ❶

↑ Textbook 5A p88

1 Solve the following calculations.

a) 24,592 − 3,470 = [ ]

TTh	Th	H	T	O
●●	●●●●	●●●●●	●●●●●●● ●●●●	●●

	TTh	Th	H	T	O
	2	4	5	9	2
−		3	4	7	0

b) 51,340 − 30,720 =

TTh	Th	H	T	O
●●●●●● ●		●●●	●●●●	

	TTh	Th	H	T	O
	5	1	3	4	0
−	3	0	7	2	0

c)

	TTh	Th	H	T	O
		4	3	6	5
−		2	4	2	3

d)

	TTh	Th	H	T	O
	7	6	1	8	5
−		5	2	2	4

e) 15,712 − 6,000 = [ ]

f) 26,318 − 11,148 = [ ]

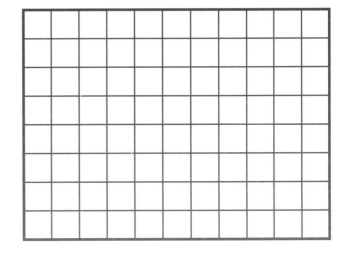

2 Work out the missing numbers.

a)

73,200	
25,000	

		TTh	Th	H	T	O	
−							

b)

48,923	
37,382	

		TTh	Th	H	T	O	
−							

3 **a)** A house costs £127,365. The house next door costs £102,724.

How much less does the house next door cost?

b) A new car costs £18,495. A motorbike costs £7,620.

How much cheaper is the motorbike than the car?

4 Fill in the missing digits.

a)

	TTh	Th	H	T	O	
		2	6	1	8	
−			4		2	
		2		4	5	0

b)

	TTh	Th	H	T	O	
			9	9		3
−		1		6	2	7
		3	5		5	

5 Three chests each contain some treasure.

CHALLENGE

- The first chest contains 18,455 coins.
- The second chest has 4,200 fewer coins than the first chest.
- The third chest has 5,120 fewer coins than the second chest.

How many coins are in each treasure chest?

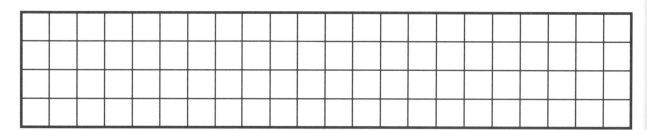

Reflect

Explain how to work out 32,728 − 14,605.

Date: _____

Subtract whole numbers with more than 4 digits ❷

→ Textbook 5A p92

1 Work out the answers to the following subtractions.

You can use the counters and place value grid to help you.

7,243 – 4,826 = ◻

Th	H	T	O
●●●●● ●●	●●	●●●●	●●●

		Th	H	T	O	
		7	2	4	3	
	–	4	8	2	6	

2 Work out the answers to the following subtractions.

a) 72,108 – 48,468 = ◻

		TTh	Th	H	T	O	
		7	2	1	0	8	
	–	4	8	4	6	8	

c)

		TTh	Th	H	T	O	
		5	3	7	0	2	
	–	4	8	9	5	3	

b)

		TTh	Th	H	T	O	
		1	2	5	9	8	
	–	1	0	9	4	8	

d)

		TTh	Th	H	T	O	
		3	4	4	2	0	
	–	2	8	0	7	3	

67

3 Work out the answers to the following subtractions.

a) Subtract 729 from 84,381

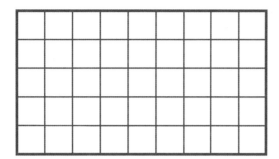

b) 729,482 – 78,359

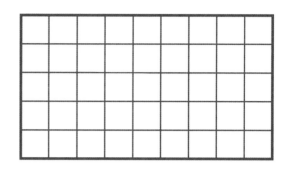

4 A ball pool contains 76,350 balls. In the first hour 18,926 balls are removed. In the second hour another 18,926 balls are removed.

How many remain in the pool now?

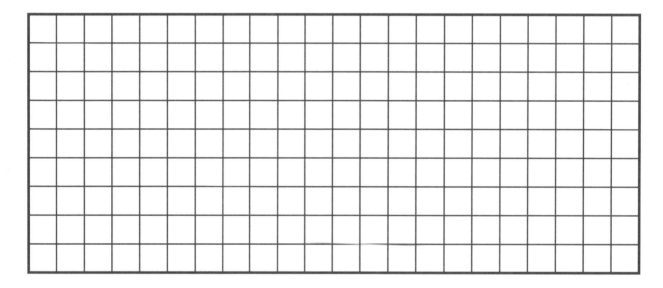

5 Fill in the missing digits.

a)

	TTh	Th	H	T	O	
			5	0	6	
–		4			2	
		2	6	7		

b)

	TTh	Th	H	T	O	
	3	9	2			
–			8	3	7	
	2	7	3	8	0	

6 Find the answers to the following calculations.

a) $2,700 - 1,375 = \boxed{}$

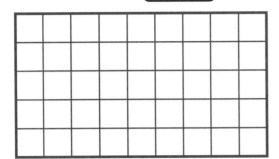

b) $27,000 - 18,904 = \boxed{}$

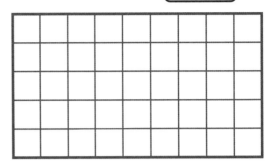

7 349,500 people attend a charity concert. There are 186,956 adults at the concert and the rest are children. Of the children who attend, 73,290 are in fancy dress.

How many children attend in ordinary clothes?

Reflect

Max subtracts a 5-digit number from a 5-digit number. It involves two exchanges.

Write a possible subtraction. Explain how you know it involves two exchanges.

Date: _____

Round to check answers

1 Use rounding to estimate the answers to the following calculations.

a) 297 + 204

297 is close to ☐.

204 is close to ☐.

☐ + ☐ = ☐

So, 297 + 204 must be close to ☐.

b) 6,985 − 1,995

6,985 is close to ☐.

1,995 is close to ☐.

☐ − ☐ = ☐

So, 6,985 − 1,995 must be close to ☐.

c) 311 + 7,189

311 is close to ☐.

7,189 is close to ☐.

☐ + ☐ = ☐

So, 311 + 7,189 must be close to ☐.

2 Bella is working out a question.

a) Use rounding to show that Bella's answer must be incorrect.

12,005 is close to [   ].

7,620 is close to [   ].

[   ] + [   ] = [   ]

		TTh	Th	H	T	O	
			1	2	0	0	5
	+		7	6	2	0	
			8	8	2	0	5

b) What mistake has Bella made?

_____

_____

c) What is the correct answer to the calculation?

12,005 + 7,620 = [   ]

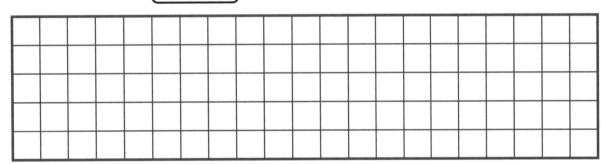

3 Estimate the answer to each of these calculations.

a) 3,395 − 207

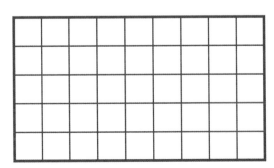

My estimate is [   ].

b) 169,995 + 50,062

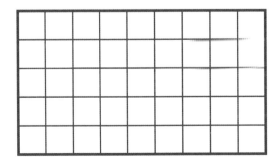

My estimate is [   ].

4 Max and Jamie are estimating the answer to 2,187 + 3,703.

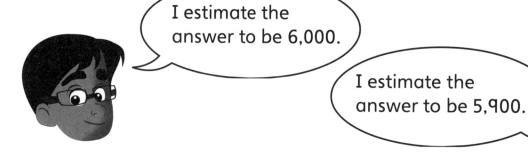

I estimate the answer to be 6,000.

I estimate the answer to be 5,900.

Explain to a partner how Max and Jamie made their estimates.

CHALLENGE

5 **a)** Estimate the answer to £19,995 + £3,941 − £4,081.

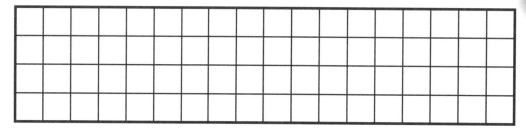

b) What is the exact answer to the calculation?

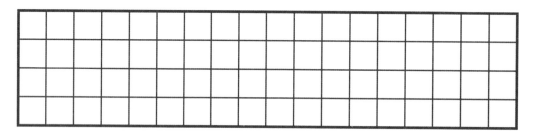

Reflect

Explain to a partner why it is useful to estimate an answer to a calculation.

Inverse operations (addition and subtraction)

→ Textbook 5A p100

1 Work out an inverse calculation to check each answer below.
Then tick the box next to the correct statement.

a)

2,704 − 1,264 = 1,440

The answer is correct. ☐

The answer is incorrect. ☐

		Th	H	T	O	
		1	4	4	0	
	+	1	2	6	4	

b)

14,600 + 1,295 = 15,995

The answer is correct. ☐

The answer is incorrect. ☐

		TTh	Th	H	T	O	
		1	5	9	9	5	
	−	1	4	6	0	0	

c)

37,010 − 18,182 = 18,468

The answer is correct. ☐

The answer is incorrect. ☐

		TTh	Th	H	T	O	
	+						

2 **a)** Write down the fact family for this part-whole model.

 +  =

 + =

 − =

 − =

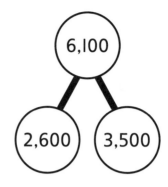

6,100

2,600   3,500

b) Complete an addition to check if this part-whole model is correct.

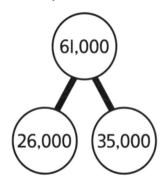

61,000

26,000   35,000

3 Spot the mistakes in these calculations.

Show the correct working for each calculation.

a)

	TTh	Th	H	T	O
	3	4	7	2	6
+	1	1	2	0	
	4	5	9	2	6

b)

	TTh	Th	H	T	O
	2	4	0	0	0
−	2	3	8	7	2
		1	8	7	2

4 Richard is working out 7,500 + 3,500 in his head.

The answer is 10,000.

a) What subtractions could he use to check that he is correct?

_____

_____

b) Explain the mistake Richard has made.

What is the correct answer to the calculation?

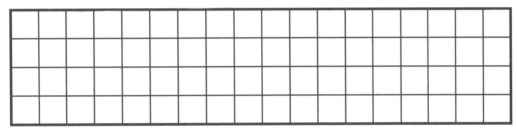

5 Mo checks a calculation by working out 764 + 13,500.

What calculation could Mo have been checking?

CHALLENGE

_____

_____

Reflect

Alex says, 'To check an answer, I will just do the calculation again.'

Is this a good idea? Why might it not always work?

_____

_____

_____

Date: _____

Multi-step addition and subtraction problems ❶

❶ Work out the missing values on the bar models below.

a)

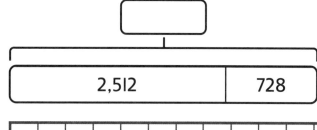

2,512	728

b)

292,500 kg

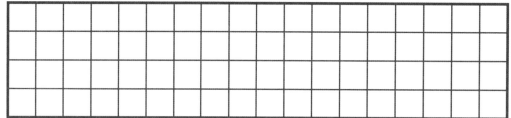

| 165,000 kg | |

c)

£5,894

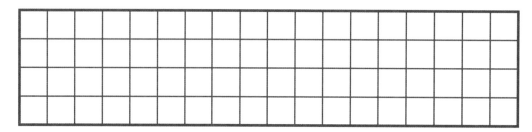

| £485 | | £2,038 |

2 What is the number at A?

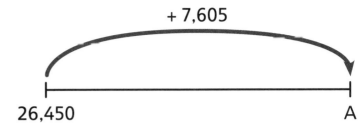

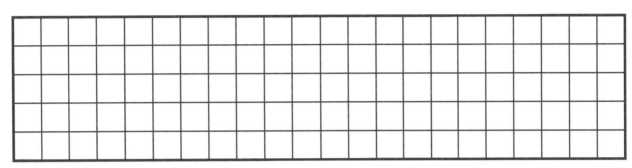

The number at A is [ ].

3 A café sells 1,308 cups of coffee on Monday.

On Tuesday, it sells 750 more cups of coffee than on Monday.

How many cups of coffee does the café sell in total over both days?

Monday [1,308]

Tuesday [ ] } ?

4 Add 3,456 and 2,922, and then subtract the total from 8,000.

5 This table shows the number of eggs sold in a supermarket in a week.

Mon	Tue	Wed	Thu	Fri	Sat	Sun
2,040	1,990	2,000	2,960	3,450	8,720	5,940

How many more eggs were sold at the weekend than during the week?

Reflect

Write a problem where you first have to add two numbers together, and then subtract a number from your answer.

Multi-step addition and subtraction problems ❷

1 A swimming pool contains 160,500 litres of water. Then 85,000 litres of water are added to the pool. Finally, 7,900 litres of water are removed from the pool.

How much water is in the pool now?

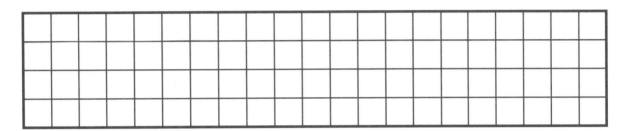

2 This two-way table shows how many toys Karl and Tex made in September and October.

	Karl	Tex
September	12,675	13,188
October	9,580	10,680

a) Tex made more toys in total. How do you know that without doing any calculations?

_____

_____

b) How many more toys did Tex make in total?

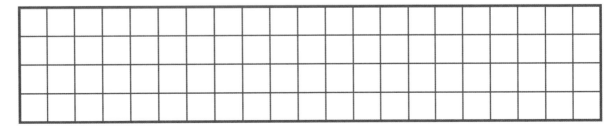

3 These three numbers add to make 30,000.

| 12,840 | 7,319 | ? |

What is the value of the missing number?

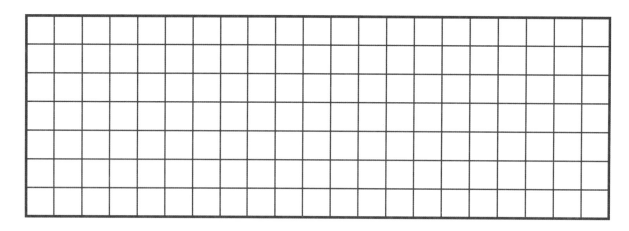

4 There are three barrels of apples.

• The first barrel contains 1,280 apples.

• The second barrel contains 480 more apples than the first barrel.

• The third barrel contains 276 fewer apples than the first barrel.

How many apples are there in total?

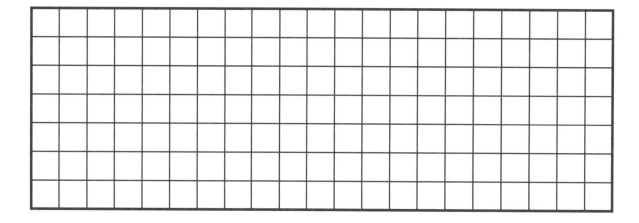

5 Kate makes jumps on a number line, adding the same amount each time.

She starts at 75,560 and the first number she gets to is 100,385.

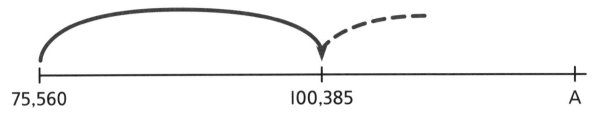

75,560   100,385   A

a) What number is at A?

b) What is the first number above 200,000 that Kate will reach?

Reflect

Discuss with a partner how you would work out which calculation has the bigger answer.

182,500 − 79,320   75,111 + 28,396

Date: _____

Solve missing number problems

1 Mo is trying to work out the missing number for this calculation in his head.

$$38 + \boxed{} = 90$$

First I work out how many I need to add on to make the next 10.

Mo

Then I work out how many 10s I need to add.

Complete the calculation that Mo might do in his head to find the answer.

$$38 + \boxed{} = 40 \qquad\qquad 40 + \boxed{} = 90$$

The missing number is $\boxed{}$.

2 Work out the missing numbers.

Use the number lines to help.

a) $24 + \boxed{} = 70$

b) $350 + \boxed{} = 800$

82

3 Jamilla is working out the missing number.

$39 +$ ☐ $= 80$

The answer is 51.

Jamilla

Jamilla is incorrect.

Why do you think Jamilla has said 51?

Discuss this with a partner.

4 Work out the missing numbers.

a) $56 +$ ☐ $= 80$

b) ☐ $+ 14 = 70$

c) $64 +$ ☐ $= 670$

d) $33 +$ ☐ $= 100$

e) $322 +$ ☐ $= 380$

f) $5,077 +$ ☐ $= 5,150$

5 Work out the missing numbers.

a) $270 +$ ☐ $= 600$

b) $740 +$ ☐ $= 1,000$

c) $2,300 +$ ☐ $= 7,000$

d) $340 +$ ☐ $= 900$

e) ☐ $+ 350 = 800$

f) $1,800 +$ ☐ $= 3,000$

g) $38 +$ ☐ $= 72$

h) $380 +$ ☐ $= 720$

i) $29 +$ ☐ $= 83$

j) $35 +$ ☐ $= 53$

6 Work out the missing numbers.

a) $70 - \boxed{} = 32$

├───┤

b) $140 - \boxed{} = 106$

├───┤

c) $140 - \boxed{} = 87$

├───┤

CHALLENGE

7 Work out the missing number.

$130 + 250 + \boxed{} = 900$

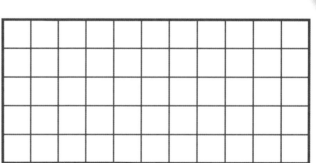

Reflect

What methods do you know to work out a missing number?

Explain to a partner.

Solve comparison problems

1 Work out the missing numbers.

a) $45 + 27 = 44 + \boxed{}$

    $45 + 27 = 43 + \boxed{}$

    $45 + 27 = 46 + \boxed{}$

    $45 + 27 = 55 + \boxed{}$

b) $315 + 264 = 313 + \boxed{}$

    $315 + 264 = 305 + \boxed{}$

    $315 + 264 = 415 + \boxed{}$

    $315 + 264 = \boxed{} + 464$

2 Work out the missing number.

$$170,000 + 250,000 = 160,000 + \boxed{}$$

Explain to a partner how you did this.

_____

_____

_____

3 Ambika is trying to work out the missing number.

249 + 176 = 239 + ☐

I have decreased 249 by 10, so the other number should also decrease by 10. The missing number is 166.

Ambika

What mistake has Ambika made?

_____

_____

4 Find the missing numbers.

a)

3,400	2,180
2,400	

b)

17,000		9,500
16,000		
18,000		

5 Work out the missing numbers.

a) $675 - 162 = 674 - \boxed{}$

b) $675 - 162 = 673 - \boxed{}$

c) $675 - 162 = 677 - \boxed{}$

d) $675 - 162 = 685 - \boxed{}$

6 Work out the missing number.

CHALLENGE

$$10{,}000 + 2{,}500 = 20{,}000 - \boxed{}$$

Explain your method to a partner.

Reflect

Which missing number problems did you find easiest?

Which did you find more challenging?

- _____
- _____
- _____

Date: _____

End of unit check

My journal

1. Make up a story problem that this bar model could be used to solve.

You are trying to work out what the ? is.

Monday | 39,480 |

Tuesday | | ? |

100,000

Ask a partner to solve your problem.

_____

_____

_____

_____

_____

_____

_____

Power check

How do you feel about your work in this unit?

Power puzzle

1 The total for each row and column is shown.

a) Work out the missing values in this table.

	20,000	50,000	40,000
60,000		32,932	
30,000	15,441		
20,000		5,966	13,197

b) Complete your own table with these totals.

Try to do this mentally.

	2,600	2,000	1,400
3,000			
2,000			
1,000			

Now make up your own table for a partner to solve.

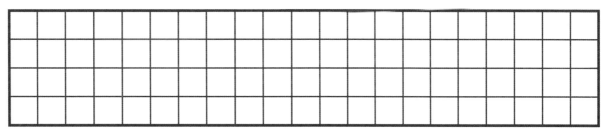

Date: _____

Multiples

1 Amelia draws diagrams to show multiples. Complete the multiplications.

a)

$3 \times 3 = \boxed{}$

b)

$\boxed{} \times 3 = \boxed{}$

c)

$\boxed{} \times 3 = \boxed{}$

These all show multiples of the number $\boxed{}$.

2 a) Shade multiples of 10 on the 100 square.

b) Using a different colour, shade multiples of 3.

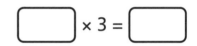

1	2	3	4	5	6	7	8	9	10
11	12	13	14	15	16	17	18	19	20
21	22	23	24	25	26	27	28	29	30
31	32	33	34	35	36	37	38	39	40
41	42	43	44	45	46	47	48	49	50
51	52	53	54	55	56	57	58	59	60
61	62	63	64	65	66	67	68	69	70
71	72	73	74	75	76	77	78	79	80
81	82	83	84	85	86	87	88	89	90
91	92	93	94	95	96	97	98	99	100

3 **a)** Write down the first ten multiples of 9.

_____

b) Write down the first five multiples of 12.

_____

c) Write down the multiples of 4 between 15 and 45.

_____

4 **a)** Circle all of the multiples of 2.

| 80 | 41 | 30 | 59 | 102 | 300 | 99 | 1 | 223 |

b) Circle all of the multiples of 5.

| 52 | 70 | 95 | 33 | 53 | 530 | 35 | 300 | 559 |

5 Fill in the next four multiples in these sequences.

a)

| 125 | 130 | 135 | | | | |

b)

| 273 | 280 | 287 | | | | |

c)

| 1,424 | 1,428 | 1,432 | | | | |

6 **a)** Can you find two numbers to go in each section of the table?

	Multiple of 2	Not a multiple of 2
Multiple of 6		
Not a multiple of 6		

b) Do any sections have no numbers? Why?

_____

_____

7 Is 12,734 a multiple of 4?

Explain how you know.

CHALLENGE

_____

_____

Reflect

Richard says that 7 is a multiple of 10, because 7 × 10 = 70. Explain his mistake.

_____

_____

_____

Common multiples

→ Textbook 5A p128

1 Complete the table for the first ten multiples of each number.

Multiples of 4	Multiple of 5

Write down all the common multiples of 4 and 5 in your list.

_____

2 Continue the lists to show the first ten multiples of 10 and 12.

| 10 | 20 | 30 | 40 | | | | | | |

| 12 | 24 | 36 | 48 | | | | | | |

Circle all the common multiples.

93

3 List the first ten multiples of the following numbers. Then find and circle the lowest common multiple of each pair of numbers.

a) 8 and 12

8									

12									

b) 5 and 10

5									

10									

c) 5 and 8

5									

8									

4 a) Find the lowest common multiple of 6 and 9.

_____

_____

b) Write the next three common multiples of 6 and 9.

_____

c) How did you work them out?

_____

_____

5 Work out the lowest common multiple of these numbers.

a) 7 and 10 _____

_____

b) 6 and 8 _____

_____

c) 3, 4 and 6 _____

_____

_____

6 Every multiple of 12 is also a multiple of 6.

Is this statement correct? Explain your answer.

CHALLENGE

_____

_____

Reflect

Explain the method you use for finding the lowest common multiple of two numbers.

_____

_____

_____

Date: _____

Factors

1 a) Write the multiplication for each array.

 ☐ × ☐ = 18

  ☐ × ☐ = 18

  ☐ × ☐ = 18

b) Write all the factors of 18 _____

2 Here is an array for 20.

a) Draw two more arrays for 20.

b) Write all the factors of 20.

_____

_____

3 Is 6 a factor of 28? Explain your answer.

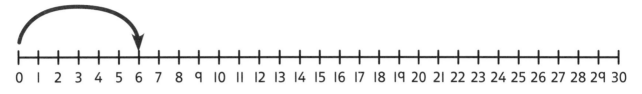

_____

_____

4 Find all the factor pairs of 24 and 36.

a) 1 × 24 = 24

2 × ☐ = 24

3 × ☐ = 24

4 × ☐ = 24

b) 1 × 36 = 36

2 × ☐ = 36

3 × ☐ = 36

4 × ☐ = 36

6 × ☐ = 36

5 **a)** Find all of the factors of 50.

b) Find all the factors of 48.

6 **a)** Shade the numbers that are factors of 100.

20   40   200   50   5   100

70   1   10   4   95

b) There are two factors of 100 missing. What are they?

The missing factors are ☐ and ☐ .

7 Kate holds a number card. Max holds a number card.

CHALLENGE

My number is a factor of your number.

Kate

Then my number must be a multiple of your number.

Max

Is this always true? Try a few examples and then explain to a partner what you have found out.

Reflect

Andy says that because 70 is an even number it has a factor of 4. Explain his mistake.

Date: _____

Common factors

1 Put ticks in the table to show the factors of 18 and 20.

Number	Factor of 18	Factor of 20
1	✓	✓
2		
3		
4		
5		
6		

2 **a)** Find all of the factors of 24.

b) Find all of the factors of 50.

c) Write the common factors of 24 and 50.

→ Textbook 5A p136

3 Write down the common factors of 15 and 20.

_____

4 **a)** Complete the sorting circles.

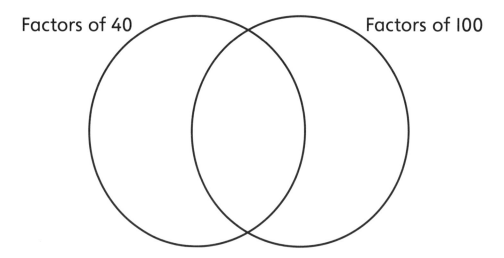

Factors of 40   Factors of 100

b) Explain to a partner where the common factors of 40 and 100 are in the sorting circles.

c) Write the common factors of 40 and 100.

_____

5 Complete the sorting circles.

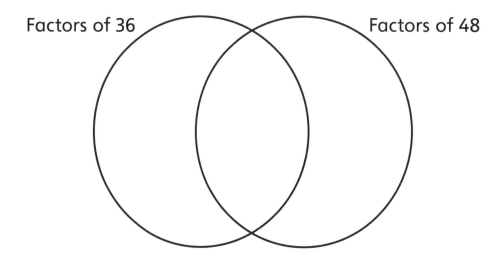

Factors of 36   Factors of 48

6 Two numbers are even.

Write down two common factors of these numbers.

_____

_____

7 The sorting circles show information about the factors of two numbers A and B.

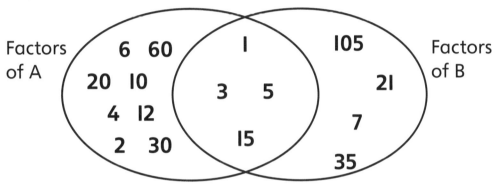

Factors of A: 6 60 20 10 4 12 2 30

3 5 15 1

Factors of B: 105 21 7 35

a) What are the common factors of A and B? _____

b) How do you know that A is an even number?

_____

c) What number is A? _____

Reflect

Every number has at least two factors.

True or False? Explain your answer.

- _____
- _____

Date: _____

Prime numbers

1 This shows 11 is not a multiple of 2.

● ● ● ● ●
● ● ● ● ● ●

Explain why 11 is a prime number.

_____

_____

_____

2 Complete the table.

- Tick all the prime numbers.

- For the numbers that are not prime, write down a multiplication that makes that number.

Number	Prime	Not Prime
10		2 × 5
11	✓	
12		
13		
14		
15		
16		
17		
18		
19		
20		

3 Place each number in the correct group.

| 2 | 5 | 21 | 24 | 25 | 31 | 39 |

Even

Prime

a) Which of the numbers is in both groups?

b) Which numbers are not in either group? _____

c) Can any other numbers join both groups? Explain your answer.

_____

_____

4 Is 99 a prime number? How do you know?

_____

_____

5 a) How do you know that 1,265 is not a prime number?

_____

_____

b) Is 3,711 a prime number?

Explain your reasoning.

_____

_____

6 **a)** Shade all of the prime numbers in this chart.

b) What do you notice about where most of the prime numbers appear?

_____

_____

_____

c) Explain why some columns have no prime numbers.

_____

_____

_____

d) Which column has the most prime numbers?

_____

_____

_____

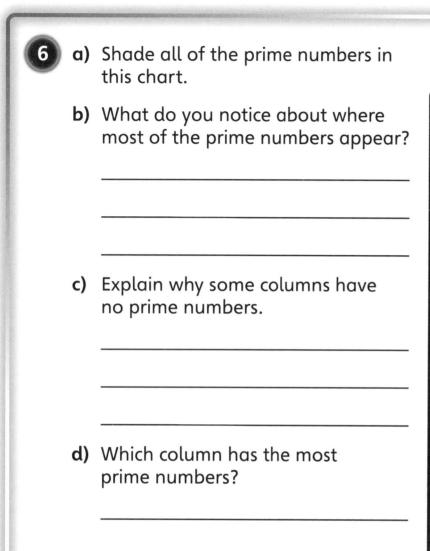

1	2	3	4	5	6
7	8	9	10	11	12
13	14	15	16	17	18
19	20	21	22	23	24
25	26	27	28	29	30
31	32	33	34	35	36
37	38	39	40	41	42
43	44	45	46	47	48
49	50	51	52	53	54
55	56	57	58	59	60
61	62	63	64	65	66
67	68	69	70	71	72
73	74	75	76	77	78
79	80	81	82	83	84
85	86	87	88	89	90
91	92	93	94	95	96
97	98	99	100	101	102

Reflect

Prove that 33 is not a prime number.

Date: _____

Square numbers

1 Complete the calculations for each square number.

a)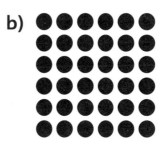

$3^2 = \boxed{} \times \boxed{} = \boxed{}$

b)

$\boxed{}$ squared $= \boxed{}^2$

$\boxed{} \times \boxed{} = \boxed{}$

2 Complete the table.

Square	Calculation
5^2	$5 \times 5 = 25$
6^2	$6 \times 6 = 36$
7^2	
8^2	
9^2	
10^2	
11^2	
12^2	

3 Draw an array of dots to show a square number between 30 and 40.

$\boxed{}^2 = \boxed{}$

4 Is 10 a square number? Draw arrays of dots to show your reasons.

5 Is Mo correct?

⬤⬤⬤⬤⬤⬤⬤⬤
⬤⬤⬤⬤⬤⬤⬤⬤

This shows that 16 is not a square number.

Mo

_____

_____

6 Shade the square numbers below.

(62)　　　(20)　　　(1)　　　(81)

(110)　　　(4)　　　(2)　　　(144)

7 **a)** Complete the table by finding all of the factors of these numbers: 9, 25 and 49.

Remember, factors are numbers that divide exactly into another number.

CHALLENGE

Number	9	25	49
All factors	1, 3, 9		
How many factors?	3		

b) Find some square numbers that have different numbers of factors.

c) Isla says, 'Only square numbers can have an odd number of factors.'

Do you agree? Explain your reasoning by using calculations or arrays.

Reflect

How many square numbers can you find between 50 and 150?

Date: _____

Cube numbers

1 Match each diagram to the correct card.

 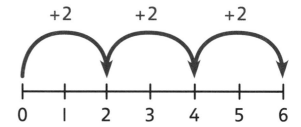

2 × 3	2^3	3 × 3 × 3	2 squared

2 Use the multilink cubes to work out the cube numbers.

a) $5^3 = \boxed{} \times \boxed{} \times \boxed{}$

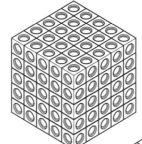

b) $\boxed{}$ cubed $= \boxed{} \times \boxed{} \times \boxed{}$

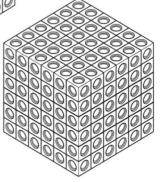

c) $\boxed{}^3 = \boxed{} \times \boxed{} \times \boxed{}$

3 Work out the following.

a) 7 cubed = ☐

b) 10^3 = ☐

c) $☐^3$ = 1

d) $☐^3$ = 0

4 Correct the following mistakes.

a) 3 is a cube number, because $1^3 = 1 + 1 + 1 = 3$

_____

_____

b) To work out 3^3, do 3 × 3 which is 9, then 9 × 9 which is 81.

_____

_____

5 Work out the following:

a) 5^3 = ☐

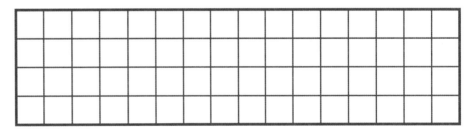

b) 8^3 = ☐

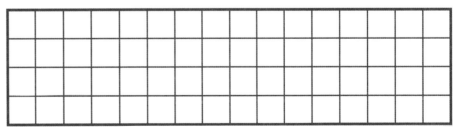

c) 20^3 = ☐

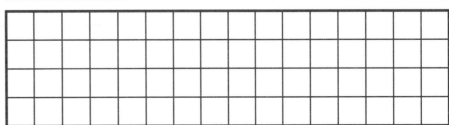

CHALLENGE

6 Luis is finding different ways to work out 4^3 by breaking up a cube.

Show working that he might use for each of the following.

a)

b)

c)

Reflect

Explain to a partner how to work out the first five cube numbers.

Multiply by 10, 100 and 1,000

1 Complete the following calculations.

a)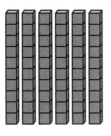

$6 \times 10 = \boxed{}$

b)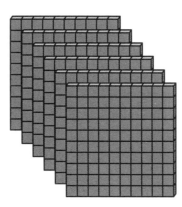

$6 \times 100 = \boxed{}$

c)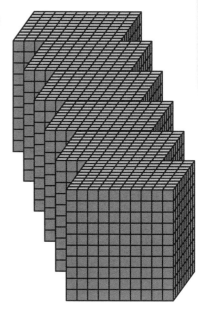

$6 \times 1,000 = \boxed{}$

d)

| 10 | 10 | 10 | 10 | 10 | 10 | 10 | 10 | 10 |

| 100 | 100 | 100 | 100 | 100 | 100 | 100 | 100 | 100 |

| 1,000 | 1,000 | 1,000 | 1,000 | 1,000 | 1,000 | 1,000 | 1,000 | 1,000 |

$9 \times 10 = \boxed{}$

$9 \times 100 = \boxed{}$

$9 \times 1,000 = \boxed{}$

2 Here is some of Reena's work.

$31 \times 10 = 310$	$40 \times 100 = 400$	$1,000 \times 12 = 12,000$
$31 \times 100 = 3,100$	$50 \times 10 = 500$	$1,000 \times 20 = 2,000$

There are two errors. Find and correct both of them.

3 Multiply each number by 10, 100 and 1,000.

The first one has been done for you.

a)

	TTh	Th	H	T	O
Number				3	7
× 10			3	7	0
× 100					
× 1,000					

b)

	TTh	Th	H	T	O
Number				7	0
× 10					
× 100					
× 1,000					

Explain to a partner what you notice.

4 Work out the following calculations.

a) $5 \times 10 = \boxed{}$

$13 \times 10 = \boxed{}$

$127 \times 10 = \boxed{}$

$10 \times 25 = \boxed{}$

b) $7 \times 100 = \boxed{}$

$28 \times 100 = \boxed{}$

$139 \times 100 = \boxed{}$

$100 \times 11 = \boxed{}$

c) $3 \times 1,000 = \boxed{}$

$14 \times 1,000 = \boxed{}$

$178 \times 1,000 = \boxed{}$

$1,000 \times 11 = \boxed{}$

d) $7 \times \boxed{} = 700$

$19 \times \boxed{} = 19,000$

$33 \times \boxed{} = 3,300$

$\boxed{} \times 116 = 1,160$

5 Complete the following calculations.

a) $5 \times 10 = \boxed{}$

$50 \times 10 = \boxed{}$

$50 \times 100 = \boxed{}$

$5 \times 1{,}000 = \boxed{}$

b) $\boxed{} \times 1{,}000 = 15{,}000$

$100 \times \boxed{} = 1{,}500$

$1{,}500 = \boxed{} \times 10$

$15{,}000 = \boxed{} \times 100$

6 Complete the following calculations.

CHALLENGE

a) $3 \times 10 \times 10 = 3 \times \boxed{}$

b) $5 \times 10 \times 10 \times 10 = 5 \times \boxed{}$

c) $6 \times 10 \times 10 = 60 \times \boxed{}$

d) $7 \times 10 \times 10 \times 10 = 70 \times \boxed{}$

e) $20 \times 10 \times 10 = 200 \times \boxed{}$

Reflect

What happens to the digits in a number when you multiply by 10, 100 and 1,000?

_____

_____

_____

113

Date: _____

Divide by 10, 100 and 1,000

1 Complete the following

a) 20 ÷ 10 = ☐

30 ÷ 10 = ☐

40 ÷ 10 = ☐

170 ÷ 10 = ☐

230 ÷ 10 = ☐

b) 200 ÷ 100 = ☐

400 ÷ 100 = ☐

700 ÷ 100 = ☐

1,200 ÷ 100 = ☐

3,600 ÷ 100 = ☐

What patterns do you notice?

_____

_____

2 Max is dividing 12,000 by 100.

What mistake has Max made?

What is the correct answer?

☐

The answer is 12.

Max

3 How many weights are needed to balance the scales?

a) 8,000 ÷ 1,000 = ☐

b) 8,000 ÷ 100 = ☐

c) 8,000 ÷ 10 = ☐

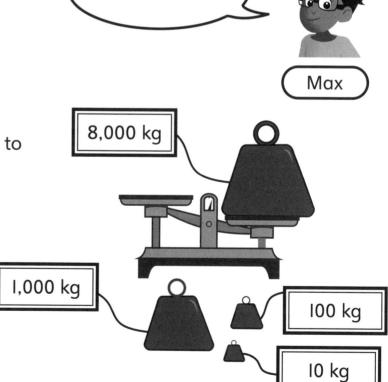

8,000 kg

1,000 kg

100 kg

10 kg

4 Divide each number by 10, 100 and 1,000.

The first one has been done for you.

a)

	TTh	Th	H	T	O
Number		6	0	0	0
÷ 10			6	0	0
÷ 100					
÷ 1,000					

c) 26,000 ÷ 1,000 = ☐

   26,000 ÷ 100 = ☐

   26,000 ÷ 10 = ☐

b)

	TTh	Th	H	T	O
Number	4	3	0	0	0
÷ 10					
÷ 100					
÷ 1,000					

d) 5,000 ÷ ☐ = 100

   5,000 ÷ ☐ = 10

   500 ÷ ☐ = 10

Explain to a partner what you notice.

5 Olivia has 2,000 marbles. She splits them into 10 equal groups, then splits each group equally into 10 jars.

a) How many marbles are in each jar? ☐

b) How many jars are there in total?

6 **a)** Complete the different solutions for:

$$\bigstar \times 10 = \triangle \div 10$$

Explain the relationship between $\bigstar$ and $\triangle$.

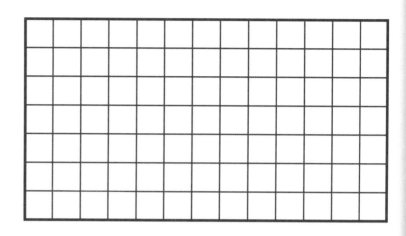

$\bigstar$	$\triangle$
5	
	7,000
	700
500	

b) Now, using your own numbers, investigate this calculation.

What relationship can you find between the symbols?

$$\heartsuit \div 10 = 10 \times 10 \times \text{☁}$$

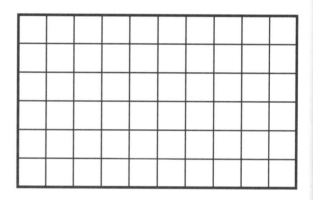

Reflect

Discuss with a partner.

Which of these is correct? How do you know? How can you check your answer?

$$3,300 \div 10 = 33$$

$$3,300 \div 100 = 33$$

Multiples of 10, 100 and 1,000

→ Textbook 5A p160

1 Work out the following calculations.

a)

$3 \times 2 = \boxed{}$

c)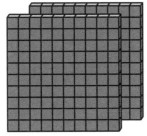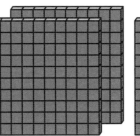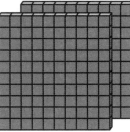

$3 \times 200 = \boxed{}$

b)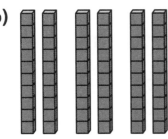

$3 \times 20 = \boxed{}$

2 Draw lines to match the diagrams to the descriptions and the correct answer. One has been done for you.

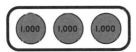

3 × 2 hundreds   12 hundreds = 1,200

2 × 3 thousands   12 tens = 120

3 × 4 hundreds   6 hundreds = 600

4 × 3 tens   6 thousands = 6,000

117

3 Work out the following calculations.

a) 5 × 3 = ☐

5 × 30 = ☐

5 × 300 = ☐

5 × 3,000 = ☐

b) 7 × 10 = ☐

7 × 20 = ☐

7 × 30 = ☐

7 × 40 = ☐

4 Use the representations to help you work out the divisions.

a)

8 ÷ 2 = ☐

b)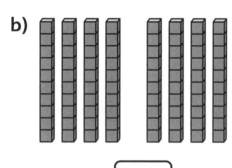

80 ÷ 2 = ☐

c)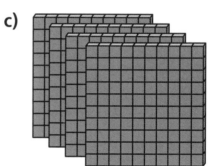

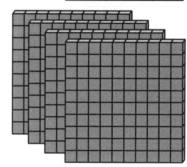

800 ÷ 2 = ☐

5 Work out the following calculations.

a) 18 ÷ 3 = ☐

180 ÷ 3 = ☐

1,800 ÷ 3 = ☐

18,000 ÷ 3 = ☐

b) 2,400 ÷ 2 = ☐

2,400 ÷ 3 = ☐

2,400 ÷ 6 = ☐

6 Complete the following calculations using facts from the multiplication tables.

a) $3 \times 700 = \boxed{}$

$5{,}000 \times 9 = \boxed{}$

$5 \times 80 = \boxed{}$

b) $1{,}200 \div \boxed{} = \boxed{}$

$150 \div 5 = \boxed{}$

$72{,}000 \div \boxed{} = \boxed{}$

7 Explain why both Ambika and Reena are incorrect.

CHALLENGE

Ambika: $4 \times 500 = 200$, as there are two zeros.

Reena: $4 \times 5 = 20$, so $40 \times 50 = 200$ because it will have two zeros.

_____

_____

Reflect

Write down two things you have noticed in this lesson.

- _____
- _____
- _____
- _____

Date: _____

End of unit check

My journal

Isla: I know 25 is a square number, so I think 250 is too.

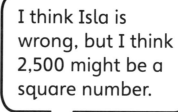

Ambika: I think Isla is wrong, but I think 2,500 might be a square number.

We need to find the factors of 250 and 2,500.

Aki

→ Textbook 5A p164

Explore whether either 250 or 2,500 is a square number.

Power check

How do you feel about your work in this unit?

Power puzzle

1 Here are 4 digit cards.

You can use any of these symbols.

Show how you can use all 4 digits to make these numbers.

a) 100

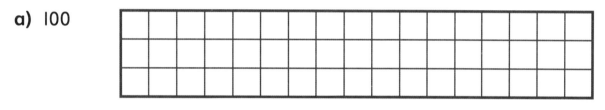

b) 64

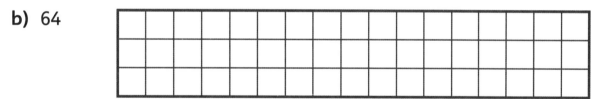

c) 600

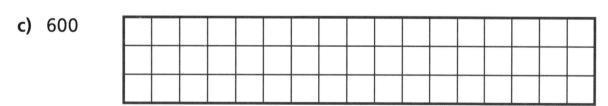

You can use the symbols as many times as you like.

Date: _____

Equivalent fractions

1 Change each diagram to show that $\frac{1}{3} = \frac{2}{6}$.

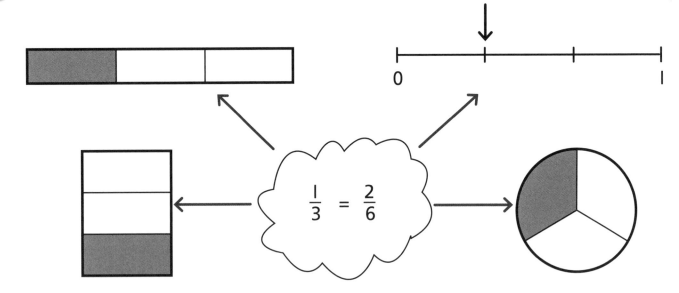

2 Complete the equivalent fractions.

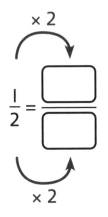

$$\frac{1}{2} = \frac{\boxed{}}{\boxed{}} \quad \times 2$$

$$\frac{1}{2} = \frac{\boxed{}}{\boxed{}} \quad \times 3$$

$$\frac{1}{2} = \frac{\boxed{}}{\boxed{}} \quad \times 5$$

I will draw diagrams to check my answers.

3 Complete the equivalent fractions.

a) $\dfrac{1}{2} = \dfrac{4}{\boxed{}}$

c) $\dfrac{1}{8} = \dfrac{3}{\boxed{}}$

e) $\dfrac{1}{9} = \dfrac{7}{\boxed{}}$

b) $\dfrac{1}{2} = \dfrac{\boxed{}}{4}$

d) $\dfrac{1}{8} = \dfrac{\boxed{}}{40}$

f) $\dfrac{1}{9} = \dfrac{\boxed{}}{72}$

4 Complete the missing denominators.

a) $\dfrac{1}{\boxed{}} = \dfrac{4}{28}$

c) $\dfrac{1}{\boxed{}} = \dfrac{6}{54}$

e) $\dfrac{1}{\boxed{}} = \dfrac{7}{63}$

b) $\dfrac{6}{42} = \dfrac{1}{\boxed{}}$

d) $\dfrac{3}{33} = \dfrac{1}{\boxed{}}$

f) $\dfrac{4}{80} = \dfrac{1}{\boxed{}}$

5 Mark Reena's work. Put a tick or a cross to show whether Reena is correct.

$\dfrac{1}{5} = \dfrac{11}{55}$ $\dfrac{1}{6} = \dfrac{4}{9}$ $\dfrac{1}{15} - \dfrac{3}{17}$ $\dfrac{1}{21} = \dfrac{2}{42}$ $\dfrac{1}{50} = \dfrac{51}{100}$

☐   ☐   ☐   ☐   ☐

123

6 **a)** Find three fractions that are equivalent to $\frac{1}{10}$.

CHALLENGE

b) Find three fractions that are equivalent to $\frac{1}{100}$.

c) Find three fractions that are equivalent to $\frac{1}{25}$.

d) Find three fractions that are equivalent to $\frac{1}{879}$.

Reflect

Explain how to make a list of fractions that are equivalent to $\frac{1}{9}$.

Date: _____

Equivalent fractions – unit and non-unit fractions

→ Textbook 5A p172

1 Divide the diagram into quarters. Then shade $\frac{1}{8}$ of the diagram.

2 Complete the equivalent fractions.

a)

$\frac{3}{5} = \frac{\boxed{}}{15}$

b)

$\frac{3}{5} = \frac{\boxed{}}{20}$

c)

$\frac{4}{5} = \frac{\boxed{}}{15}$

d)

$\frac{4}{5} = \frac{\boxed{}}{20}$

3 Complete the equivalent fractions.

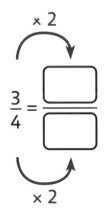

$\frac{3}{4} = \frac{\boxed{}}{\boxed{}}$ ×2

$\frac{3}{4} = \frac{\boxed{}}{\boxed{}}$ ×3

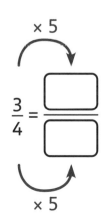

$\frac{3}{4} = \frac{\boxed{}}{\boxed{}}$ ×5

4 Complete the equivalent fractions.

a) $\dfrac{2}{5} = \dfrac{4}{\boxed{}}$

d) $\dfrac{2}{9} = \dfrac{4}{\boxed{}}$

g) $\dfrac{2}{13} = \dfrac{4}{\boxed{}}$

b) $\dfrac{2}{5} = \dfrac{\boxed{}}{25}$

e) $\dfrac{2}{9} = \dfrac{\boxed{}}{36}$

h) $\dfrac{2}{13} = \dfrac{\boxed{}}{130}$

c) $\dfrac{\boxed{}}{15} = \dfrac{12}{30}$

f) $\dfrac{\boxed{}}{8} = \dfrac{3}{4}$

i) $\dfrac{8}{\boxed{}} = \dfrac{64}{72}$

5 Write three equivalent fractions for each fraction.

a) $\dfrac{2}{11} = \dfrac{\boxed{}}{\boxed{}} = \dfrac{\boxed{}}{\boxed{}} = \dfrac{\boxed{}}{\boxed{}}$

c) $\dfrac{6}{11} = \dfrac{\boxed{}}{\boxed{}} = \dfrac{\boxed{}}{\boxed{}} = \dfrac{\boxed{}}{\boxed{}}$

b) $\dfrac{4}{11} = \dfrac{\boxed{}}{\boxed{}} = \dfrac{\boxed{}}{\boxed{}} = \dfrac{\boxed{}}{\boxed{}}$

d) $\dfrac{10}{11} = \dfrac{\boxed{}}{\boxed{}} = \dfrac{\boxed{}}{\boxed{}} = \dfrac{\boxed{}}{\boxed{}}$

6 Complete the equivalent fractions.

CHALLENGE

a) ×3

$$\frac{1}{5} = \frac{\boxed{}}{\boxed{}}$$

×3

c) ÷2

$$\frac{\boxed{}}{16} = \frac{5}{\boxed{}}$$

÷2

e)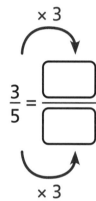

÷10 $\frac{\boxed{}}{10} = \frac{\boxed{}}{30}$ ÷10

b)

×5 $\left(\frac{3}{\boxed{}} = \frac{4}{\boxed{}} \right)$ ×5

d) ×3

$$\frac{3}{5} = \frac{\boxed{}}{\boxed{}}$$

×3

f) ÷3

$$\frac{\boxed{}}{\boxed{}} = \frac{9}{30}$$

÷3

Reflect

Write down as many fractions equivalent to $\frac{10}{15}$ as you can.

Explain your method.

_____

_____

_____

Date: _____

Equivalent fractions – families of equivalent fractions

 a) Complete the equivalent fractions to match each diagram.

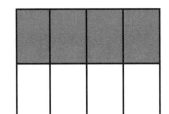

$$\frac{1}{2} = \frac{\boxed{}}{8}$$

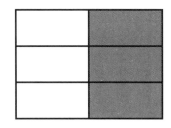

$$\frac{1}{2} = \frac{3}{\boxed{}}$$

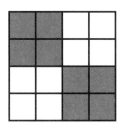

$$\frac{1}{2} = \frac{\boxed{}}{\boxed{}}$$

b) Draw lines on each diagram to show different fractions equivalent to $\frac{2}{3}$.

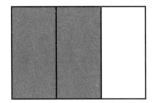

$$\frac{2}{3} = \frac{\boxed{}}{6}$$

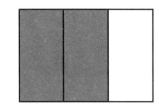

$$\frac{2}{3} = \frac{\boxed{}}{\boxed{}}$$

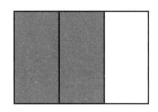

$$\frac{2}{3} = \frac{\boxed{}}{\boxed{}}$$

c) Shade the diagrams to match each fraction.

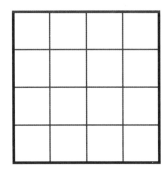

$$\frac{1}{4}$$

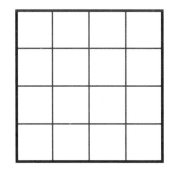

$$\frac{2}{8}$$

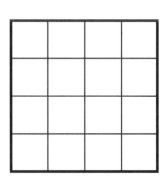

$$\frac{3}{12}$$

2 Write the equivalent fractions.

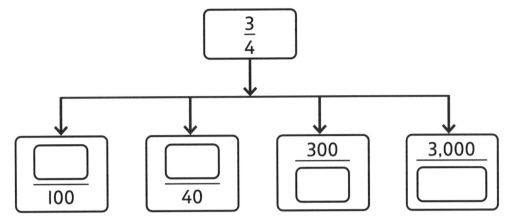

$$\frac{3}{4}$$

$$\frac{\boxed{}}{100} \qquad \frac{\boxed{}}{40} \qquad \frac{300}{\boxed{}} \qquad \frac{3{,}000}{\boxed{}}$$

3 Complete the equivalent fractions.

a) $\dfrac{2}{5} = \dfrac{\boxed{}}{10} = \dfrac{\boxed{}}{15} = \dfrac{\boxed{}}{20} = \dfrac{\boxed{}}{25}$

b) $\dfrac{3}{10} = \dfrac{\boxed{}}{\boxed{}} = \dfrac{\boxed{}}{\boxed{}} = \dfrac{\boxed{}}{\boxed{}}$

c) $\dfrac{3}{8} = \dfrac{\boxed{}}{\boxed{}} = \dfrac{\boxed{}}{\boxed{}} = \dfrac{\boxed{}}{\boxed{}}$

4 Complete the different equivalent fractions for each fraction shown.

a) $\dfrac{80}{240} = \dfrac{8}{\boxed{}} = \dfrac{\boxed{}}{6} = \dfrac{200}{\boxed{}}$

b) $\dfrac{3}{12} = \dfrac{6}{\boxed{}} = \dfrac{\boxed{}}{32} = \dfrac{\boxed{}}{\boxed{}}$

5 Which is correct? Show your reasoning.

$$\frac{8}{12} = \frac{12}{16} \qquad\qquad \frac{8}{20} = \frac{6}{15}$$

_____

_____

6 Use each set of digit cards to create two equivalent fractions.

a) 100   4   25   16

$$\frac{\boxed{}}{\boxed{}} = \frac{\boxed{}}{\boxed{}} \qquad \frac{\boxed{}}{\boxed{}} = \frac{\boxed{}}{\boxed{}}$$

b) 5   6   10   12

$$\frac{\boxed{}}{\boxed{}} = \frac{\boxed{}}{\boxed{}} \qquad \frac{\boxed{}}{\boxed{}} = \frac{\boxed{}}{\boxed{}}$$

c) 9   30   10   27

$$\frac{\boxed{}}{\boxed{}} = \frac{\boxed{}}{\boxed{}} \qquad \frac{\boxed{}}{\boxed{}} = \frac{\boxed{}}{\boxed{}}$$

Explain what you notice.

_____

_____

Reflect

Explain two different methods you can use to find equivalent fractions.

- _____
- _____

Date: _____

Improper fractions to mixed numbers

→ Textbook 5A p180

1 **a)** Each weight has a mass of $\frac{1}{2}$ kg. Write the total mass of the weights as a mixed number.

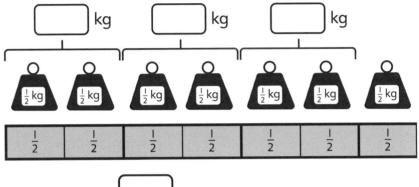

$$\frac{7}{2} \text{ kg} = \boxed{} \frac{\boxed{}}{\boxed{}} \text{ kg}$$

b) Each glass holds $\frac{1}{4}$ litre of juice. Write the total volume of juice as a mixed number.

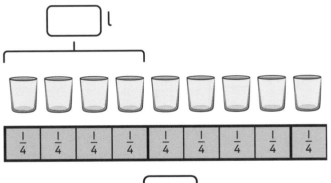

$$\frac{9}{4} \text{ litres} = \boxed{} \frac{\boxed{}}{\boxed{}} \text{ litres}$$

c) Aki has $\frac{11}{3}$ metres of ribbon. Write this as a mixed number.

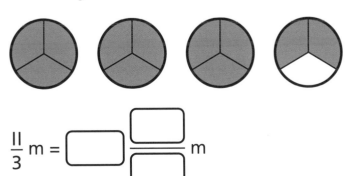

$$\frac{11}{3} \text{ m} = \boxed{} \frac{\boxed{}}{\boxed{}} \text{ m}$$

2 Max has 15 quarter circles. He joins them together to make whole circles. Complete the statements.

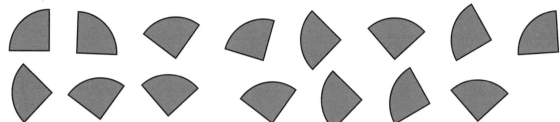

[ ] quarters make one whole circle.

Max has $\dfrac{15}{4}$ circles in total. That is [ ] $\dfrac{\square}{\square}$ whole circles.

3 Convert these improper fractions to mixed numbers.

a) $\dfrac{13}{3} =$ [ ] $\dfrac{\square}{\square}$

e) $\dfrac{13}{5} =$ [ ] $\dfrac{\square}{\square}$

i) $\dfrac{15}{5} =$ [ ] $\dfrac{\square}{\square}$

b) $\dfrac{13}{4} =$ [ ] $\dfrac{\square}{\square}$

f) $\dfrac{14}{5} =$ [ ] $\dfrac{\square}{\square}$

j) $\dfrac{16}{5} =$ [ ] $\dfrac{\square}{\square}$

c) $\dfrac{11}{7} =$ [ ] $\dfrac{\square}{\square}$

g) $\dfrac{20}{3} =$ [ ] $\dfrac{\square}{\square}$

k) $\dfrac{37}{5} =$ [ ] $\dfrac{\square}{\square}$

d) $\dfrac{15}{4} =$ [ ] $\dfrac{\square}{\square}$

h) $\dfrac{25}{8} =$ [ ] $\dfrac{\square}{\square}$

l) $\dfrac{19}{3} =$ [ ] $\dfrac{\square}{\square}$

4 Circle the fractions that are whole numbers.

$\dfrac{12}{4}$ $\dfrac{24}{5}$ $\dfrac{60}{12}$ $\dfrac{40}{7}$ $\dfrac{66}{6}$ $\dfrac{12}{8}$

CHALLENGE

5 Find different solutions to this problem.

$$\frac{\blacktriangle}{10} = \blacksquare \frac{\bigstar}{10}$$

> I will just pick some numbers to start with and then change one to make the calculation correct.

Discuss with a partner.

Reflect

How would you convert $\frac{17}{3}$ to a mixed number?

Date: _____

Mixed numbers to improper fractions

1 Convert the mixed numbers into improper fractions.

a)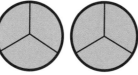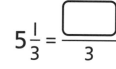

$5\dfrac{1}{3} = \dfrac{\boxed{}}{3}$

b)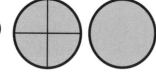

$4\dfrac{1}{4} = \dfrac{\boxed{}}{\boxed{}}$

c)

$6\dfrac{3}{5} = \dfrac{\boxed{}}{\boxed{}}$

2 Match each mixed number to the improper fraction.

$3\dfrac{1}{4}$

$\dfrac{9}{4}$

$\dfrac{13}{4}$

$\dfrac{7}{2}$

$\dfrac{5}{2}$

3 Write the improper fraction for each mixed number shown.

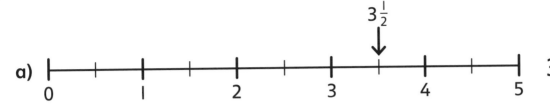

a)
$3\frac{1}{2} = \dfrac{\boxed{}}{\boxed{}}$

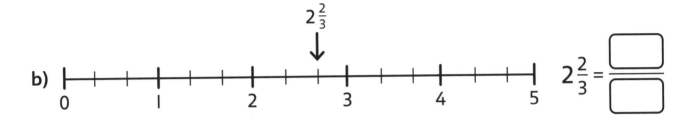

b)
$2\frac{2}{3} = \dfrac{\boxed{}}{\boxed{}}$

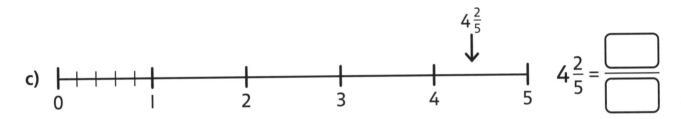

c)
$4\frac{2}{5} = \dfrac{\boxed{}}{\boxed{}}$

4 Convert the mixed numbers into improper fractions.

a) $4\frac{1}{5} = \dfrac{\boxed{}}{\boxed{}}$

b) $4\frac{3}{5} = \dfrac{\boxed{}}{\boxed{}}$

c) $4\frac{4}{5} = \dfrac{\boxed{}}{\boxed{}}$

d) $3\frac{2}{3} = \dfrac{\boxed{}}{\boxed{}}$

e) $2\frac{7}{10} = \dfrac{\boxed{}}{\boxed{}}$

f) $3\frac{1}{8} = \dfrac{\boxed{}}{\boxed{}}$

g) $2\frac{4}{7} = \dfrac{\boxed{}}{\boxed{}}$

h) $9\frac{1}{11} = \dfrac{\boxed{}}{\boxed{}}$

i) $5\frac{3}{4} = \dfrac{\boxed{}}{\boxed{}}$

5 A waiter has $3\frac{1}{2}$ litres of juice. A glass holds $\frac{1}{4}$ of a litre. How many glasses can the waiter fill?

6 Complete the missing numbers.

CHALLENGE

a) $\dfrac{\boxed{}}{4} = 3\frac{1}{2}$

$\dfrac{\boxed{}}{8} = 3\frac{1}{2}$

$\dfrac{21}{\boxed{}} = 3\frac{1}{2}$

b) $4\frac{5}{10} = \dfrac{\boxed{}}{2}$

$4\frac{6}{10} = \dfrac{\boxed{}}{5}$

$4\frac{7}{10} = \dfrac{\boxed{}}{20}$

$4\frac{8}{10} = \dfrac{\boxed{}}{15}$

I used my knowledge of equivalent fractions.

Reflect

Draw a diagram to show why $2\frac{4}{5} = \frac{14}{5}$.

Compare fractions less than I

1 Write < or > to compare the numbers. Shade the diagrams to check your answers.

a) $\frac{1}{6}$ ◯ $\frac{3}{6}$

$\frac{1}{6}$

$\frac{3}{6}$

c) $\frac{4}{5}$ ◯ $\frac{3}{5}$

$\frac{4}{5}$

$\frac{3}{5}$

b) $\frac{2}{3}$ ◯ $\frac{2}{6}$

$\frac{2}{3}$

$\frac{2}{6}$

d) $\frac{5}{8}$ ◯ $\frac{3}{4}$

$\frac{5}{8}$

$\frac{3}{4}$

2 Choose <, > or = to complete each statement.

a) $\frac{1}{4}$ ◯ $\frac{1}{8}$

e) $\frac{3}{10}$ ◯ $\frac{9}{10}$

b) $\frac{5}{24}$ ◯ $\frac{5}{6}$

f) $\frac{1}{100}$ ◯ $\frac{1}{4}$

c) $\frac{3}{12}$ ◯ $\frac{1}{4}$

g) $\frac{1}{3}$ ◯ $\frac{5}{18}$

d) $\frac{11}{20}$ ◯ $\frac{3}{5}$

h) $\frac{41}{100}$ ◯ $\frac{10}{25}$

3 Bella says, 'I used these diagrams to compare $\frac{4}{5}$ and $\frac{6}{10}$. It looks like $\frac{6}{10}$ is bigger.'

$\frac{4}{5}$

$\frac{6}{10}$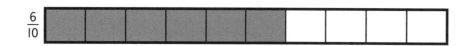

a) Explain her mistake.

_____

_____

b) Use these diagrams to show why $\frac{2}{3} > \frac{5}{9}$.

4 Use each card once to complete all the statements correctly.

| 1 | 9 | 12 | 5 |

$\dfrac{2}{5} > \dfrac{\boxed{}}{15}$ $\dfrac{\boxed{}}{8} < \dfrac{1}{4}$ $\dfrac{6}{\boxed{}} < \dfrac{3}{4}$ $\dfrac{1}{\boxed{}} < \dfrac{5}{18}$

5 Compare the fractions using <, > or =.

CHALLENGE

a) $\dfrac{1}{7} \bigcirc \dfrac{51}{364}$

b) $\dfrac{5}{6} \bigcirc \dfrac{111}{132}$

c) $\dfrac{5}{9} \bigcirc \dfrac{548}{981}$

Reflect

Describe to a partner two or three different methods for comparing fractions.

Agree on when to use each method.

Share your ideas with the class.

Date: _____

Order fractions less than 1

1 Sort these fractions into the table.

$\frac{5}{6}$ $\frac{1}{4}$ $\frac{9}{14}$ $\frac{3}{10}$ $\frac{25}{40}$ $\frac{4}{9}$ $\frac{8}{15}$

Less than $\frac{1}{2}$	Greater than $\frac{1}{2}$

Discuss your method with a partner.

2 Sort these fractions into the table.

$\frac{2}{18}$ $\frac{4}{50}$ $\frac{10}{80}$ $\frac{3}{32}$ $\frac{2}{16}$ $\frac{11}{100}$ $\frac{6}{100}$

$< \frac{1}{10}$	$> \frac{1}{10}$

3 **a)** Complete the equivalent fractions.

$$\frac{2}{3} = \frac{\boxed{}}{12}$$

$$\frac{5}{6} = \frac{\boxed{}}{12}$$

b) Put these three fractions in order from smallest to greatest.

$$\boxed{\frac{2}{3}}\qquad \boxed{\frac{5}{6}}\qquad \boxed{\frac{7}{12}}$$

$$\boxed{\frac{}{}}, \boxed{\frac{}{}}, \boxed{\frac{}{}}$$

4 Write each set of fractions in order from greatest to smallest.

a) $\boxed{\frac{3}{4}}\quad \boxed{\frac{3}{8}}\quad \boxed{\frac{7}{8}}$ $\qquad \boxed{\frac{}{}}, \boxed{\frac{}{}}, \boxed{\frac{}{}}$

b) $\boxed{\frac{1}{2}}\quad \boxed{\frac{5}{6}}\quad \boxed{\frac{5}{12}}$ $\qquad \boxed{\frac{}{}}, \boxed{\frac{}{}}, \boxed{\frac{}{}}$

c) $\boxed{\frac{3}{4}}\quad \boxed{\frac{7}{10}}\quad \boxed{\frac{17}{20}}\quad \boxed{\frac{4}{5}}$ $\qquad \boxed{\frac{}{}}, \boxed{\frac{}{}}, \boxed{\frac{}{}}, \boxed{\frac{}{}}$

5 Max is trying to find all the possible missing numbers for each question.

$\frac{5}{9} > \frac{\boxed{}}{18}$

$\frac{\boxed{}}{6} < \frac{12}{18}$

Max says, 'I think one of these has more solutions than the other.'

Do you agree? Discuss your answer with a partner.

6 Write three different fractions that are in the shaded section of each number line.

$\frac{1}{3} < \frac{\boxed{}}{\boxed{}} < \frac{2}{3}$ $\frac{1}{3} < \frac{\boxed{}}{\boxed{}} < \frac{2}{3}$ $\frac{1}{3} < \frac{\boxed{}}{\boxed{}} < \frac{2}{3}$

Reflect

Use the cards to make three fractions. You can only use each card once.

Put the fractions in order.

Choose carefully to show the different skills you need to compare fractions.

142

Compare and order fractions greater than 1

 a) Place each fraction on the number line.

     $2\frac{3}{4}$

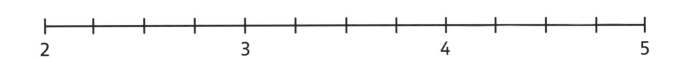

b) Write the fractions from part a) in order from smallest to greatest.

2 In each pair, circle the diagram that represents the larger number.

a)

      or

b)

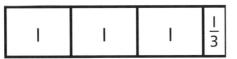   or

c)

       or

143

3 Kate and Lee are cycling laps around a track.

Kate has completed $5\frac{3}{4}$ laps. Lee has completed $5\frac{3}{8}$ laps.

Who has cycled farther? Show this using the diagrams.

Kate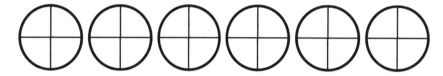

Lee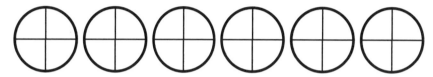

_____ has cycled farther.

4 Use <, > or = to complete each statement.

a) $3\frac{1}{5} \bigcirc 3\frac{4}{5}$

c) $\frac{15}{5} \bigcirc 3\frac{3}{5}$

e) $4\frac{2}{6} \bigcirc \frac{23}{6}$

b) $\frac{13}{5} \bigcirc \frac{17}{5}$

d) $4\frac{2}{5} \bigcirc \frac{23}{5}$

f) $\frac{23}{7} \bigcirc 4\frac{2}{7}$

5 Complete each statement.

a) $2\frac{7}{8} \bigcirc 4\frac{3}{4}$

d) $\frac{31}{5} \bigcirc \frac{31}{10}$

g) $\frac{21}{5} \bigcirc 2\frac{1}{5}$

b) $3\frac{2}{3} \bigcirc 3\frac{1}{6}$

e) $\frac{41}{6} \bigcirc \frac{41}{2}$

h) $\frac{31}{10} \bigcirc 3\frac{1}{10}$

c) $5\frac{1}{5} \bigcirc 5\frac{2}{10}$

f) $\frac{21}{2} \bigcirc \frac{41}{4}$

i) $5\frac{1}{3} \bigcirc \frac{31}{6}$

6 **a)** Aki and Kate are guessing a mystery number.

 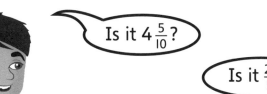 

Is it $4\frac{5}{10}$?

Is it $\frac{21}{5}$?

One of these guesses is too low. One is too high.

Write three different fractions the mystery number could be.

_____

Order these fractions – Aki's, Bella's and the three you have written.

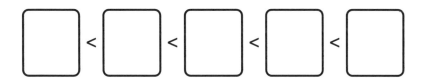

b) Write five different fractions between $3\frac{3}{8}$ and $\frac{53}{16}$.

_____

Reflect

Explain two different methods for comparing $\frac{8}{3}$ and $2\frac{1}{6}$.

Date: _____

End of unit check

My journal

Here are the number cards 1 to 20.

a) Choose 6 cards to make 3 fractions that are all equivalent.

b) Choose 6 cards to make 3 fractions greater than $\frac{1}{2}$.

c) Choose 6 cards to make 3 fractions less than $\frac{1}{5}$.

Discuss your method with a partner.

Power check

How do you feel about your work in this unit?

Power play

$\frac{2}{12}$	$\frac{25}{100}$	$\frac{11}{11}$	$1\frac{2}{3}$	$\frac{8}{20}$	$1\frac{1}{5}$
$\frac{9}{12}$	$\frac{8}{2}$	$\frac{50}{20}$	$\frac{3}{9}$	$\frac{10}{8}$	$\frac{6}{9}$
$\frac{10}{10}$	$\frac{1}{3}$	$\frac{2}{10}$	$\frac{50}{100}$	$\frac{4}{8}$	$\frac{3}{3}$
3	$\frac{12}{9}$	$\frac{10}{2}$	$\frac{1}{2}$	$\frac{50}{25}$	$\frac{8}{12}$
$\frac{9}{15}$	$1\frac{1}{2}$	$\frac{100}{100}$	$\frac{9}{6}$	$\frac{9}{6}$	$\frac{10}{12}$
$\frac{40}{20}$	1	$\frac{3}{2}$	6	$\frac{8}{10}$	$\frac{8}{8}$

- Play with a partner. You will need two dice and coloured counters (one colour for each player).

- Take turns to throw both dice. Choose one number as the numerator and one number as the denominator to make a fraction.

- Find an equivalent fraction on the board, and cover it with your coloured counter.

- The winner is the first to get four counters in a row (horizontal, vertical or diagonal).

> How can you identify the numbers that are better used as a denominator or as a numerator?

Date: _____

Add and subtract fractions

1 Work out the following calculations.

a) $\frac{2}{5} + \frac{1}{5} = \frac{\boxed{}}{\boxed{}}$

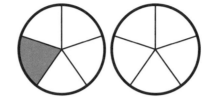

b) $\frac{3}{8} + \frac{3}{8} = \frac{\boxed{}}{\boxed{}}$

c) $\frac{9}{10} - \frac{7}{10} = \frac{\boxed{}}{\boxed{}}$

2 Work out each of the following calculations.

a) $\frac{5}{9} + \frac{3}{9} = \frac{\boxed{}}{\boxed{}}$

b) $\frac{7}{9} - \frac{2}{9} = \frac{\boxed{}}{\boxed{}}$

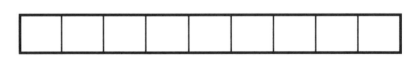

c) $\frac{2}{7} + \frac{2}{7} + \frac{2}{7} = \frac{\boxed{}}{\boxed{}}$

3 Complete each calculation.

a) $\dfrac{3}{9} + \dfrac{4}{9} = \dfrac{\boxed{}}{\boxed{}}$

d) $\dfrac{3}{10} + \dfrac{4}{10} = \dfrac{\boxed{}}{\boxed{}}$

g) $\dfrac{4}{9} - \dfrac{1}{9} = \dfrac{\boxed{}}{\boxed{}}$

b) $\dfrac{4}{9} + \dfrac{3}{9} = \dfrac{\boxed{}}{\boxed{}}$

e) $\dfrac{3}{12} + \dfrac{4}{12} = \dfrac{\boxed{}}{\boxed{}}$

h) $\dfrac{4}{10} - \dfrac{1}{10} = \dfrac{\boxed{}}{\boxed{}}$

c) $\dfrac{5}{9} + \dfrac{3}{9} = \dfrac{\boxed{}}{\boxed{}}$

f) $\dfrac{3}{20} + \dfrac{4}{20} = \dfrac{\boxed{}}{\boxed{}}$

i) $\dfrac{4}{11} - \dfrac{2}{11} = \dfrac{\boxed{}}{\boxed{}}$

4 Work out the missing parts of the calculations.

a) $\dfrac{3}{8} + \dfrac{\boxed{}}{\boxed{}} = \dfrac{7}{8}$

c) $\dfrac{7}{12} - \dfrac{\boxed{}}{\boxed{}} = \dfrac{1}{12}$

e) $\dfrac{3}{8} + \dfrac{\boxed{}}{\boxed{}} = \dfrac{5}{8}$

b) $\dfrac{17}{20} - \dfrac{\boxed{}}{\boxed{}} = \dfrac{3}{20}$

d) $\dfrac{2}{8} + \dfrac{\boxed{}}{\boxed{}} + \dfrac{2}{8} = \dfrac{5}{8}$

f) $\dfrac{\boxed{}}{\boxed{}} - \dfrac{5}{21} = \dfrac{8}{21}$

5 Work out the missing numbers.

a) $\dfrac{3}{8} + \dfrac{\boxed{}}{8} = 1$

d) $1 - \dfrac{7}{12} = \dfrac{\boxed{}}{12}$

b) $\dfrac{\boxed{}}{9} + \dfrac{7}{9} = 1$

e) $1 - \dfrac{\boxed{}}{3} = \dfrac{2}{3}$

c) $1 - \dfrac{4}{5} = \dfrac{\boxed{}}{5}$

f) $1 - \dfrac{\boxed{}}{10} = \dfrac{1}{10}$

149

6 Draw lines to join the fractions that sum to I.

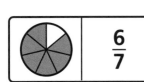

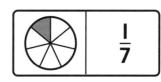

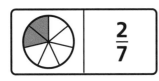

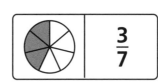

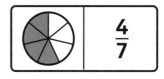

Explain how you made your choices.

_____

_____

7 Explain whether or not this calculation is correct.

$$\frac{5}{8} + \frac{3}{8} - \frac{5}{6} = \frac{1}{6}$$

_____

_____

Reflect

Write five different additions or subtractions with an answer of $\frac{13}{20}$.

- _____
- _____
- _____

Add fractions within 1

→ Textbook 5A p208

1 Work out the following calculations.

a) $\frac{2}{3} + \frac{1}{6}$

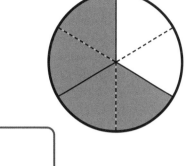

$\frac{2}{3}$ is equivalent to $\frac{\boxed{}}{6}$

b) $\frac{3}{8} + \frac{1}{4}$

$\frac{1}{4} = \frac{\boxed{}}{8}$

c) $\frac{4}{9} + \frac{1}{3}$

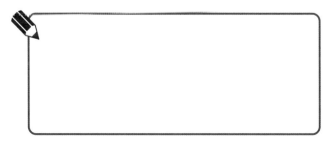

$\frac{1}{3} = \frac{\boxed{}}{9}$

2 Work out the following calculations.

a) $\frac{7}{12} + \frac{1}{4} = \frac{\boxed{}}{\boxed{}}$

c) $\frac{3}{4} + \frac{1}{20} = \frac{\boxed{}}{\boxed{}}$

b) $\frac{3}{5} + \frac{9}{25} = \frac{\boxed{}}{\boxed{}}$

d) $\frac{7}{20} + \frac{1}{2} = \frac{\boxed{}}{\boxed{}}$

3 Bella has some flowers. She gives $\frac{1}{5}$ of the flowers to Olivia and $\frac{7}{10}$ of the flowers to her grandma.

What fraction of the flowers has Bella given away?

4 What fraction of each circle is shaded in total?

a)

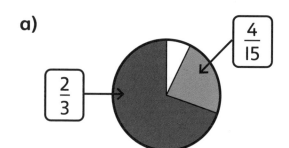

b)

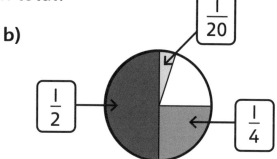

5 Work out the missing fractions.

CHALLENGE

a) $\dfrac{1}{3} + \dfrac{\boxed{}}{\boxed{}} = \dfrac{11}{12}$

b) $\dfrac{1}{4} + \dfrac{1}{12} + \dfrac{\boxed{}}{\boxed{}} = \dfrac{9}{24}$

Reflect

Discuss with a partner the mistake in this calculation.

$$\dfrac{1}{4} + \dfrac{5}{8} = \dfrac{6}{12}$$

Date: _____

Add fractions with a total greater than I

→ Textbook 5A p212

1 a) Work out $\frac{5}{6} + \frac{1}{3}$.

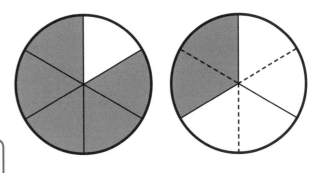

$$\frac{1}{3} = \frac{\boxed{}}{6}$$

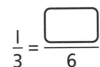

b) Work out $\frac{1}{2} + \frac{9}{10}$.

$$\frac{1}{2} = \frac{\boxed{}}{10}$$

2 Danny adds two fractions.

What is the missing fraction?

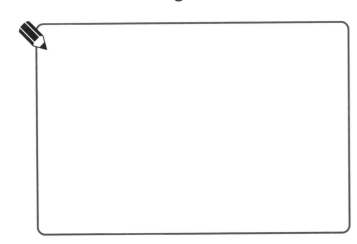

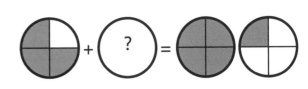

$$\frac{3}{4} + \frac{\boxed{}}{\boxed{}} = 1\frac{1}{4}$$

3 Calculate the missing numbers.

a)

$+\frac{5}{9}$

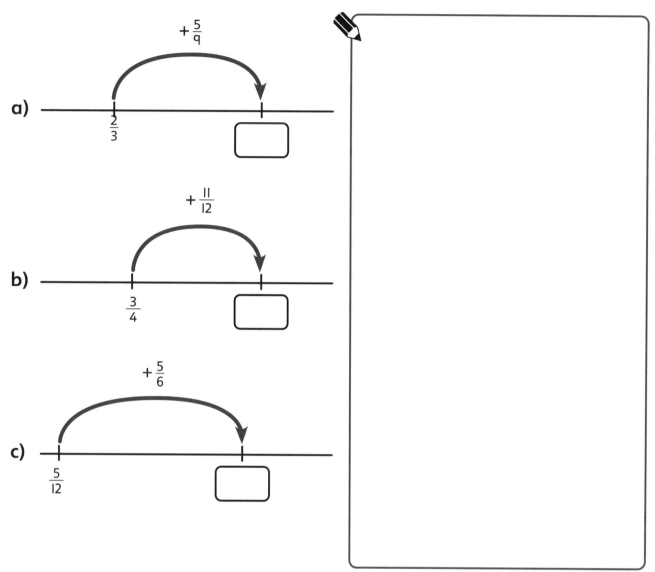

$\frac{2}{3}$

b)

$+\frac{11}{12}$

$\frac{3}{4}$

c)

$+\frac{5}{6}$

$\frac{5}{12}$

4 What is the total amount of juice in the two bottles, in litres?

$\frac{3}{4}$ litre $\frac{7}{20}$ litre

5 Work out these fraction additions.

a) $\frac{7}{10} + \frac{11}{20}$

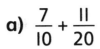

b) $\frac{11}{15} + \frac{4}{5}$

6 Work out the missing fractions.

CHALLENGE

a) $\frac{1}{2} + \dfrac{\boxed{}}{\boxed{}} = \frac{17}{12}$

b) $\frac{2}{3} + \dfrac{\boxed{}}{\boxed{}} = \frac{17}{12}$

c) $\frac{5}{6} + \dfrac{\boxed{}}{\boxed{}} = 1\frac{1}{2}$

Reflect

Max is working out $\frac{2}{3} + \frac{7}{9}$. He says the answer is $\frac{9}{12}$.

What mistake has Max made? What should the answer be?

Date: _____

Add to a mixed number

→ Textbook 5A p216

1 Add more to $2\frac{1}{3}$.

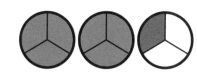

a) $2\frac{1}{3} + \frac{1}{3} = \boxed{} \dfrac{\boxed{}}{\boxed{}}$

b) $2\frac{1}{3} + 4 = \boxed{} \dfrac{\boxed{}}{\boxed{}}$

c) $2\frac{1}{3} + 1\frac{1}{3} = \boxed{} \dfrac{\boxed{}}{\boxed{}}$

2 Add more to $1\frac{2}{9}$.

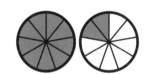

a) $1\frac{2}{9} + 8 = \boxed{} \dfrac{\boxed{}}{\boxed{}}$

b) $1\frac{2}{9} + 9 = \boxed{} \dfrac{\boxed{}}{\boxed{}}$

c) $1\frac{2}{9} + \frac{6}{9} = \boxed{} \dfrac{\boxed{}}{\boxed{}}$

3 Work out

a) $2\frac{3}{8} + \frac{1}{2} = \boxed{} \dfrac{\boxed{}}{\boxed{}}$

b) $2\frac{3}{8} + 1\frac{1}{4} = \boxed{} \dfrac{\boxed{}}{\boxed{}}$

4 Work out the following.

a) $5\frac{1}{8} + \frac{3}{4} = \boxed{}\,\dfrac{\boxed{}}{\boxed{}}$

b) $4\frac{1}{6} + \frac{1}{3} = \boxed{}\,\dfrac{\boxed{}}{\boxed{}}$

5 Work out the following by adding more.

a) $2\frac{1}{4} + \frac{5}{8} = \boxed{}\,\dfrac{\boxed{}}{\boxed{}}$

b) $\frac{7}{10} + 1\frac{1}{2} = \boxed{}\,\dfrac{\boxed{}}{\boxed{}}$

c) $4\frac{2}{5} + \frac{3}{20} = \boxed{}\,\dfrac{\boxed{}}{\boxed{}}$

d) $\frac{7}{16} + 4\frac{3}{4} = \boxed{}\,\dfrac{\boxed{}}{\boxed{}}$

6 Draw lines to match the additions that have equal totals.

$2\frac{7}{8} + \frac{1}{2}$

$2\frac{3}{4} + \frac{5}{8}$

$2\frac{3}{4} + \frac{7}{8}$

$2\frac{6}{8} + \frac{2}{8} + \frac{5}{8}$

$2 + \frac{1}{8} + \frac{2}{8}$

$\frac{7}{8} + \frac{7}{8} + \frac{5}{8}$

Reflect

What is $\frac{1}{2}$ more than each of these numbers? Discuss with a partner.

3 $4\frac{1}{2}$ $9\frac{1}{4}$ $11\frac{3}{4}$

Date: _____

Add two mixed numbers

1 Olivia walks $2\frac{1}{4}$ km on Monday. On Tuesday she walks $1\frac{3}{8}$ km.

How far does she walk in total?

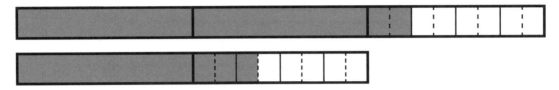

Add the wholes: $2 + 1 = \boxed{}$

Find a common denominator: $\dfrac{1}{4} = \dfrac{\boxed{}}{8}$

Add the parts: $\dfrac{1}{4} + \dfrac{3}{8} = \dfrac{\boxed{}}{8} + \dfrac{3}{8} = \dfrac{\boxed{}}{8}$

Olivia walks $\boxed{} \dfrac{\boxed{}}{\boxed{}}$ km in total.

2 Work out $3\frac{3}{5} + 2\frac{9}{10}$.

Add the wholes:

Find a common denominator: $\dfrac{3}{5} = \dfrac{\boxed{}}{10}$

Add the parts: $\dfrac{3}{5} + \dfrac{9}{10}$

$3\dfrac{3}{5} + 2\dfrac{9}{10} = \boxed{} \dfrac{\boxed{}}{\boxed{}}$

3 Work out

a) $2\frac{1}{4} + 1\frac{5}{8} = \boxed{}\dfrac{\boxed{}}{\boxed{}}$

b) $3\frac{7}{10} + 1\frac{1}{2} = \boxed{}\dfrac{\boxed{}}{\boxed{}}$

4 Work out the missing values.

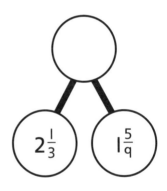

5 Washing powder is sold in two sizes.

What is the mass of the two boxes.

$2\frac{7}{12}$ kg $1\frac{2}{3}$ kg

6 Complete each addition.

a) $4\frac{2}{5} + 2\frac{9}{10} = $

b) $3\frac{1}{4} + 6\frac{11}{12} = $

7 What is the missing fraction?

CHALLENGE

$2\frac{3}{4} + \dfrac{\square}{\square} = 3\frac{7}{12}$

Reflect

Kate is adding $13\frac{2}{5}$ and $4\frac{7}{50}$.

She says, 'I think it is easier to add the wholes and the parts instead of converting to improper fractions.'

Discuss with a partner whether you agree with Kate.

Subtract fractions within 1

→ Textbook 5A p224

1 Use the diagrams to complete each calculation.

a) $\dfrac{1}{2} - \dfrac{1}{8} = \dfrac{\boxed{}}{\boxed{}}$

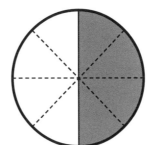

b) $\dfrac{7}{12} - \dfrac{1}{3} = \dfrac{\boxed{}}{\boxed{}}$

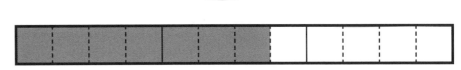

2 Work out the following.

a) $\dfrac{3}{4} - \dfrac{1}{2} = \dfrac{\boxed{}}{\boxed{}}$

c) $\dfrac{9}{10} - \dfrac{1}{2} = \dfrac{\boxed{}}{\boxed{}}$

b) $\dfrac{5}{6} - \dfrac{1}{2} = \boxed{}\dfrac{\boxed{}}{\boxed{}}$

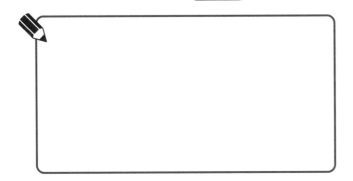

d) $\dfrac{17}{20} - \dfrac{1}{2} = \boxed{}\dfrac{\boxed{}}{\boxed{}}$

3 How much more water is in Jug A than Jug B?

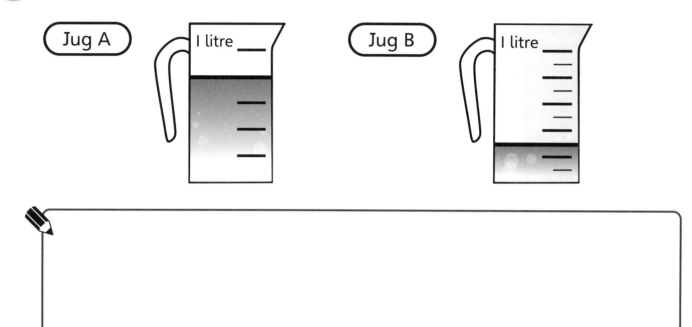

4 a) What is the total length of these strips?

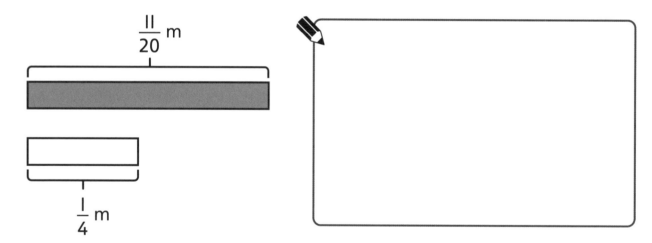

b) How much shorter is the white strip than the shaded strip, in metres?

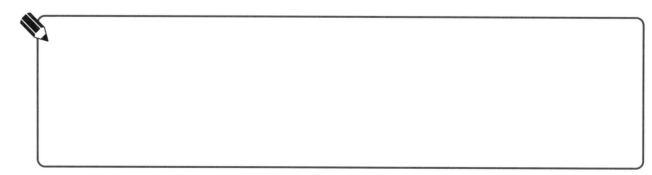

5 Work out

a) $\frac{1}{2} - \frac{1}{10} - \frac{1}{20} =$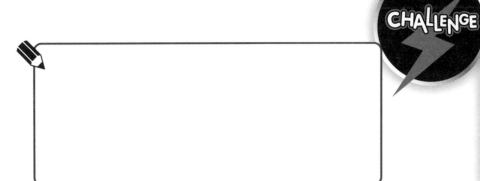

b) $\frac{1}{3} - \frac{1}{9} - \frac{1}{90} =$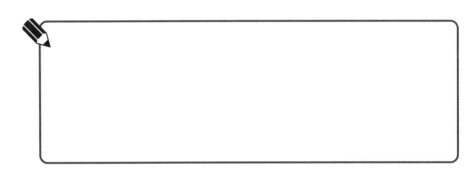

c) $\frac{1}{2} - \frac{1}{4} - \frac{1}{8} - \frac{1}{16} =$

Reflect

Write three different subtractions that have an answer of $\frac{1}{4}$.

Date: _____

Subtract from a mixed number

1 Work out $2\frac{7}{9} - \frac{5}{9}$.

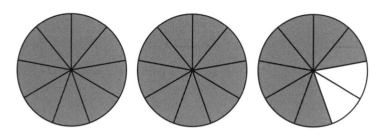

$$\frac{7}{9} - \frac{5}{9} = \frac{\boxed{}}{\boxed{}}$$

So, $2\frac{7}{9} - \frac{5}{9} = \boxed{}\frac{\boxed{}}{\boxed{}}$

2 a) Work out $3\frac{7}{8} - \frac{1}{4}$.

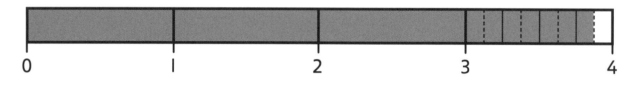

$$3\frac{7}{8} - \frac{1}{4} = 3\frac{7}{8} - \frac{\boxed{}}{8}$$

$$= 3\frac{\boxed{}}{8}$$

b) Work out $3\frac{7}{8} - \frac{1}{2}$.

$$3\frac{7}{8} - \frac{1}{2} = 3\frac{7}{8} - \frac{\boxed{}}{8}$$

$$= 3\frac{\boxed{}}{8}$$

c) Work out

$$3\frac{7}{8} - 1 = \boxed{}\frac{\boxed{}}{\boxed{}}$$

$$3\frac{7}{8} - \frac{7}{8} = \boxed{}\frac{\boxed{}}{\boxed{}}$$

3 A bakery sells cherry pies.

Each pie is cut into 12 slices.

The bakery has $2\frac{7}{12}$ pies left.

A customer buys $\frac{1}{3}$ of a pie.

How many pies are left?

4 Work out the following questions. Draw a diagram if this will help.

a) $2\frac{3}{4} - \frac{1}{2}$

c) $2\frac{3}{4} - \frac{3}{8}$

b) $1\frac{7}{10} - \frac{1}{2}$

d) $1\frac{7}{10} - \frac{3}{5}$

5 Work out

a) $4\frac{5}{8} - \frac{\square}{\square} = 4\frac{1}{8}$

c) $\square\frac{\square}{\square} - \frac{1}{9} = 3\frac{7}{9}$

b) $\square\frac{\square}{\square} - \frac{2}{9} = 3\frac{5}{9}$

d) $8\frac{7}{12} - \frac{\square}{\square} = 8$

6 Two TV shows last $2\frac{7}{8}$ hours in total.

Adverts take up $\frac{1}{4}$ of an hour in total.

The first show lasts $\frac{1}{2}$ an hour not including adverts.

How long does the second show last not including adverts?

CHALLENGE

Reflect

How do you know that $2\frac{3}{5} - \frac{3}{10}$ is greater than 2?

Date: _____

Subtract from a mixed number – breaking the whole

→ Textbook 5A p232

1 Use the fraction strips to help you work out the following.

a) $3\frac{2}{5} - \frac{4}{5} = 2\frac{\boxed{}}{5}$

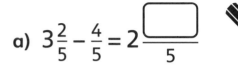

b) $2\frac{3}{8} - \frac{7}{8} = 1\frac{\boxed{}}{\boxed{}}$

2 Work out the missing fractions.

a) $1\frac{2}{7} - \frac{\boxed{}}{7} = \frac{6}{7}$

c) $1\frac{2}{7} - \frac{\boxed{}}{7} = \frac{2}{7}$

b) $1\frac{2}{7} - \frac{\boxed{}}{7} = \frac{4}{7}$

d) $1\frac{2}{7} - \frac{\boxed{}}{7} = \frac{8}{7}$

3 Work out

a) $4\frac{1}{4} - \frac{7}{8} = 3\frac{\boxed{}}{8}$

b) $2\frac{3}{5} - \frac{9}{10} = \boxed{}\frac{\boxed{}}{\boxed{}}$

4 Calculate the following.

a) $5\frac{1}{3} - \frac{7}{9} = \boxed{}\frac{\boxed{}}{\boxed{}}$

b) $5\frac{1}{3} - \frac{11}{12} = \boxed{}\frac{\boxed{}}{\boxed{}}$

c) $7\frac{2}{14} - \frac{3}{7} = \boxed{}\frac{\boxed{}}{\boxed{}}$

5 3 sandwiches are each cut into 8 pieces.

Lexi eats $\frac{5}{8}$ of one of the sandwiches.

Danny eats I more piece than Lexi.

How many sandwiches are left?

6 Work out what fractions the symbols represent.

CHALLENGE

$$2\frac{1}{2} - \blacktriangle = 1\frac{11}{12}$$

$$3\frac{5}{6} - \blacktriangle = 4\frac{1}{3} - \bullet$$

$\blacktriangle = \dfrac{\boxed{}}{\boxed{}}$ $\bullet = \boxed{}\dfrac{\boxed{}}{\boxed{}}$

Reflect

Discuss with a partner how you subtract $\frac{9}{10}$ from $2\frac{2}{5}$.

Date: _____

Subtract two mixed numbers

1 Work out

$$3\frac{5}{6} - 1\frac{1}{3} = \boxed{}\frac{\boxed{}}{\boxed{}}$$

2 Work out

$$4\frac{3}{4} - 2\frac{5}{8} = \boxed{}\frac{\boxed{}}{\boxed{}}$$

3 Work out

$$4\frac{1}{2} - 2\frac{7}{8} = \boxed{}\frac{\boxed{}}{\boxed{}}$$

4 Max runs $5\frac{1}{2}$ miles.

Emma runs $3\frac{7}{10}$ miles.

How many more miles does Max run?

5 Calculate the following:

a) $5\frac{3}{11} - 1\frac{7}{11} = $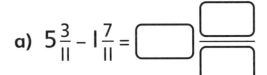

c) $5\frac{4}{5} - 3\frac{13}{15} = $

b) $5\frac{5}{12} - \frac{7}{12} = $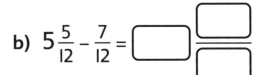

d) $2\frac{7}{18} - 1\frac{2}{3} = $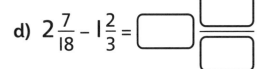

6 Circle the calculations that have an answer that is less than 2.

$4\frac{2}{5} - 2\frac{1}{5}$ $7\frac{8}{9} - 6\frac{1}{9}$

$5\frac{1}{8} - 3$ $2\frac{4}{5} - \frac{3}{10}$

$4\frac{1}{9} - 2\frac{1}{3}$ $6\frac{5}{8} - 4\frac{19}{24}$

7 Three towns lie in a straight line.

The distance between town A and town B is $4\frac{1}{2}$ km.

The distance between town A and town C is $6\frac{9}{10}$ km.

How far apart could towns B and C be? Draw a diagram to help.

CHALLENGE

Reflect

Aki writes this calculation. Discuss with a partner the mistake he has made.

$4\frac{1}{12} - 2\frac{3}{4} = 4\frac{1}{12} - 2\frac{9}{12} = 2\frac{8}{12}$

Solve fraction problems

1 Alex is reading a book.

She reads $\frac{1}{3}$ of the book on Monday.

She reads $\frac{1}{6}$ of the book on Tuesday.

What fraction of the book has she read in total?

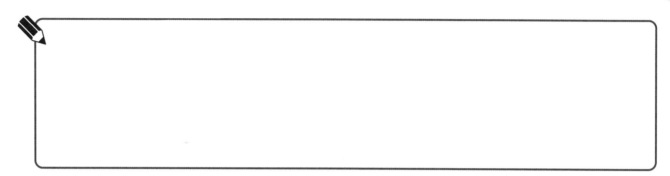

2 A rabbit eats $\frac{3}{5}$ of a bag of carrots in the morning.

In the afternoon he eats $\frac{3}{10}$ of the bag.

a) What fraction of the bag does the rabbit eat in total?

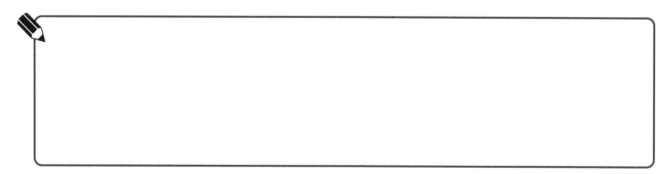

b) What fraction of the bag does the rabbit have left?

3 Kate uses these two bags of compost on her vegetable garden.

How much compost does Kate use in total?

Compost $2\frac{1}{2}$ kg

Compost $4\frac{1}{6}$ kg

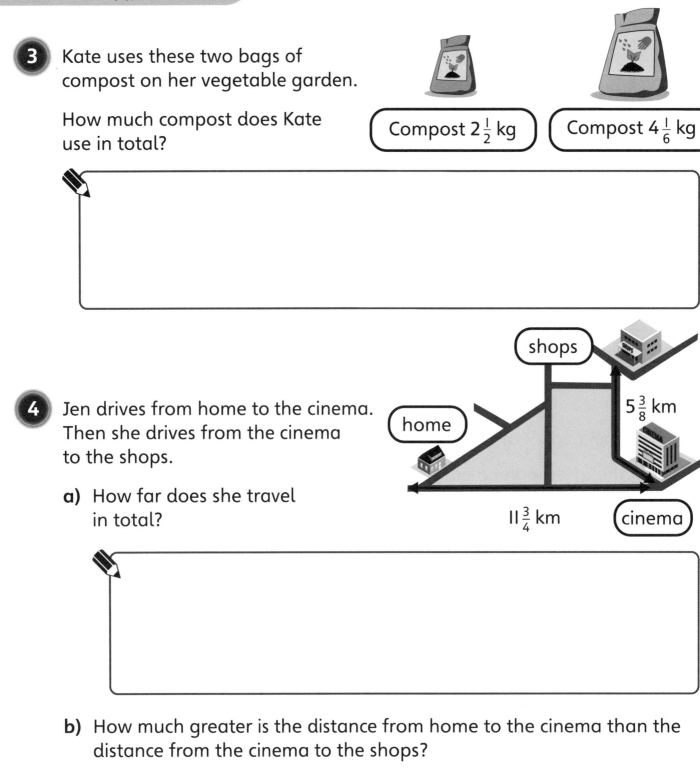

4 Jen drives from home to the cinema. Then she drives from the cinema to the shops.

shops

home

$5\frac{3}{8}$ km

$11\frac{3}{4}$ km

cinema

a) How far does she travel in total?

b) How much greater is the distance from home to the cinema than the distance from the cinema to the shops?

5 Complete the fraction pyramid.

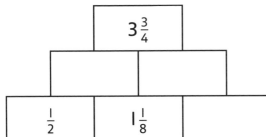

Work out the number above by adding the two fractions below.

Reflect

Write a word problem for this calculation.

$2\frac{3}{5} - 1\frac{9}{10}$

What is the answer to your problem?

Date: _____

Solve multi-step fraction problems

1. Ebo spends $\frac{4}{9}$ of his pocket money on a present and $\frac{1}{3}$ of his pocket money on a comic book. What fraction of his pocket money does he have left?

2. Leo divides a rectangle into three equal parts and shades one of the parts. He then divides one of the parts into three more equal parts and shades one of them.

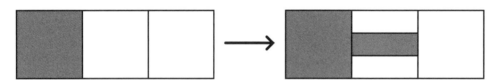

a) What fraction of the shape is now shaded?

b) Explain your method.

_____

_____

3 Max has a 3 kg bag of oats. He uses $\frac{1}{2}$ kg to make some porridge.

He uses $2\frac{3}{8}$ kg to make some flapjacks. How many kilograms of oats are left in the bag?

4 Kate used $2\frac{1}{3}$ metres of ribbon to tie a present.

Another present needed $\frac{1}{9}$ of a metre more ribbon than the first.

How much ribbon did Kate use in total?

5 Work out the missing numbers.

a) $\frac{1}{5} + \frac{\boxed{}}{15} = \frac{7}{15}$ c) $\frac{1}{5} + \frac{\boxed{}}{15} = \frac{1}{3}$

b) $\frac{1}{5} + \frac{\boxed{}}{15} = \frac{4}{15}$ d) $\frac{1}{5} + \frac{\boxed{}}{15} = 1$

6 What is the difference between A and B? Show your method.

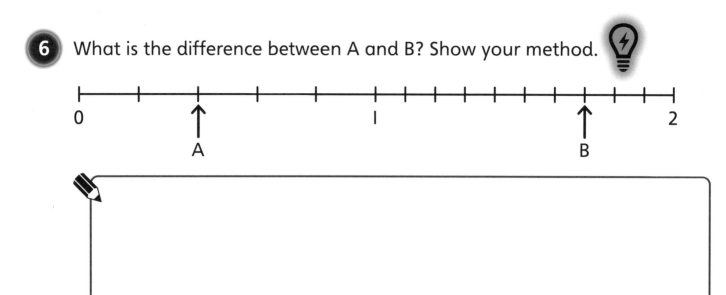

7 The perimeters of the two triangles are equal. What is the length of the missing side?

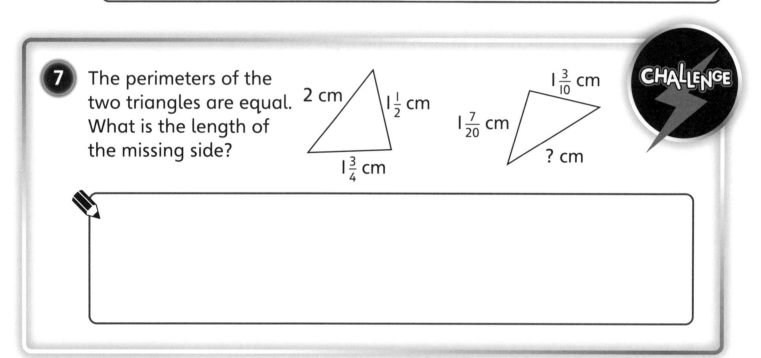

Reflect

Which question did you find most challenging? What did you learn from answering that question?

Date: _____

End of unit check

My journal

1 **a)** Explain and show how you would add these two fractions.

$8\frac{11}{12}$ and $7\frac{3}{4}$

_____

_____

_____

_____

_____

b) Explain and show how you would find the difference between these two fractions.

$12\frac{1}{12}$ and $11\frac{5}{6}$

_____

_____

_____

_____

_____

2 Last week Max drank $4\frac{1}{6}$ litres of milk.

This week he drank $1\frac{2}{3}$ litres less.

How much milk did he drink in total in the last two weeks?

Power check

How do you feel about your work in this unit?

Power puzzle

Work out the following fraction calculations,

$\dfrac{1}{2} + \dfrac{1}{4} = \dfrac{\boxed{}}{\boxed{}}$

$\dfrac{1}{2} + \dfrac{1}{4} + \dfrac{1}{8} = \dfrac{\boxed{}}{\boxed{}}$

$\dfrac{1}{2} + \dfrac{1}{4} + \dfrac{1}{8} + \dfrac{1}{16} = \dfrac{\boxed{}}{\boxed{}}$

$\dfrac{1}{2} + \dfrac{1}{4} + \dfrac{1}{8} + \dfrac{1}{16} + \dfrac{1}{32} = \dfrac{\boxed{}}{\boxed{}}$

What do you notice? Write down the next two calculations.

Can you find five fractions that have a sum of 1? All the fractions must have different denominators. Explain your method.

My power points

Put a tick against the topics you have learnt about. Show how confident you are with each one by giving it a number on a scale of 1 to 3.

1 = not at all confident;
2 = getting there;
3 = very confident

Unit 1
I have learnt how to …

☐ Use Roman numerals up to 10,000 ☐

☐ Count in 1,000s to 10,000 ☐

☐ Round numbers within 10,000 ☐

☐ Use a number line to 100,000 ☐

☐ Compare and order numbers to 100,000 ☐

☐ Partition numbers to 1,000,000 ☐

Unit 2
I have learnt how to …

☐ Use a number line to 1,000,000 ☐

☐ Compare and order numbers to 1,000,000 ☐

☐ Round numbers within 1,000,000 ☐

☐ Round numbers to the nearest 10, 100 and 1,000 ☐

Unit 3
I have learnt how to …

☐ Add whole numbers with more than 4 digits ☐

☐ Subtract whole numbers with more than 4 digits ☐

☐ Use rounding to check answers ☐

☐ Add and subtract using mental methods ☐

☐ Complete mixed additions and subtraction problems ☐

☐ Solve missing number problems ☐

☐ Solve comparison problems ☐

Unit 4

I have learnt how to ...

☐ Find a multiple of a given number ☐

☐ Find factors of a given number ☐

☐ Identify prime numbers ☐

☐ Recognise square numbers up to 100 ☐

☐ Work out cube numbers ☐

☐ Use inverse operations ☐

☐ Multiply whole numbers by 10, 100 and 1,000 ☐

☐ Divide whole numbers by 10, 100 and 1,000 ☐

☐ Multiply and divide by multiples of 10, 100 and 1,000 ☐

Unit 5

I have learnt how to ...

☐ Identify unit fractions ☐

☐ Convert improper fractions to mixed numbers ☐

☐ Convert mixed numbers to improper fractions ☐

☐ Compare and order fractions less than 1 ☐

Unit 6

I have learnt how to ...

☐ Add and subtract fractions ☐

☐ Add mixed numbers ☐

☐ Solve fraction problems ☐

☐ Solve multi-step fraction problems ☐

Keep up the good work!

Notes

Squared paper

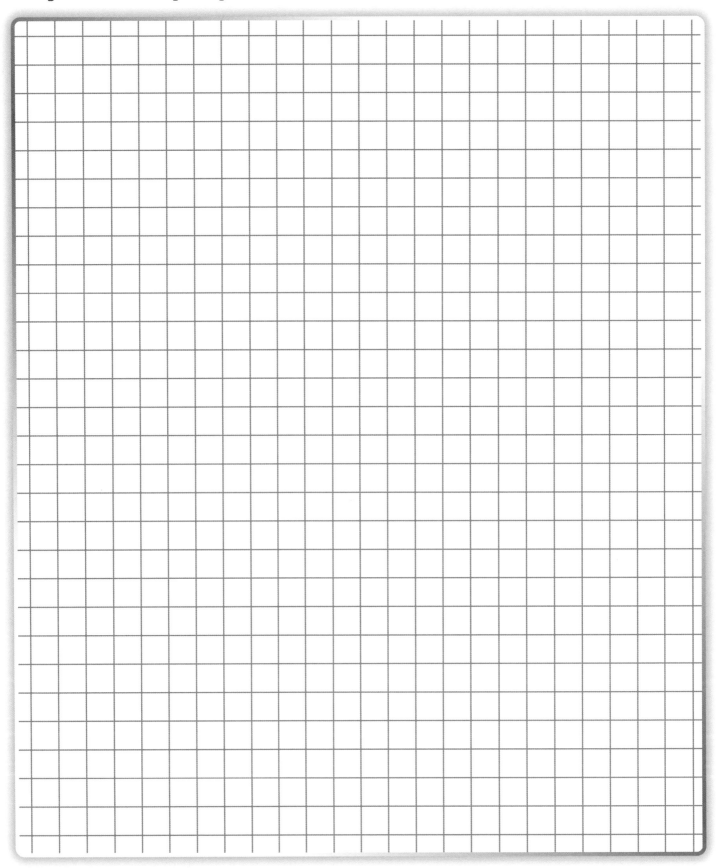

Square dotted paper

Squared paper

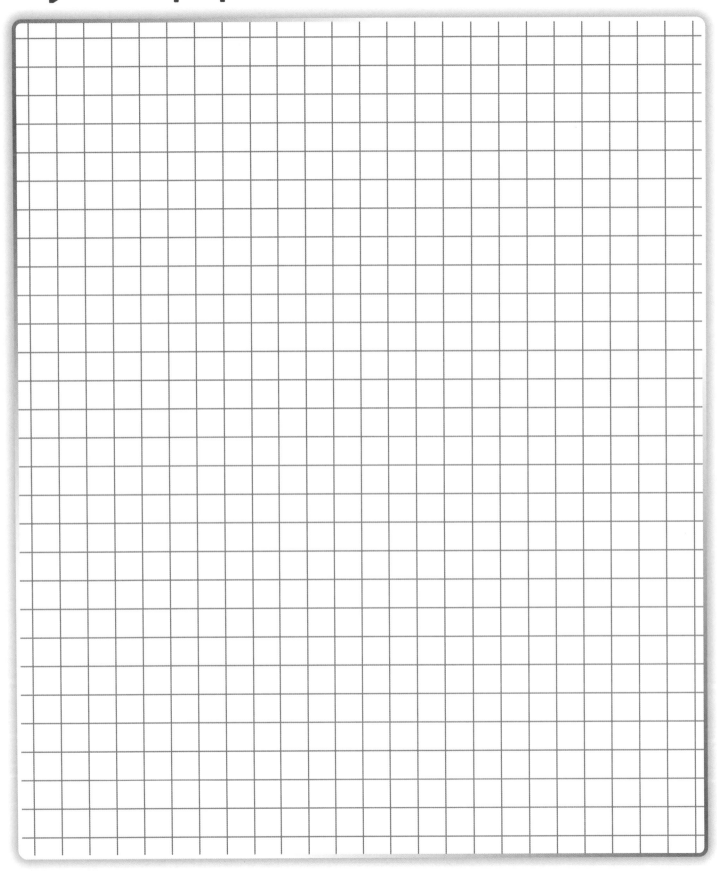

Square dotted paper

Published by Pearson Education Limited, 80 Strand, London, WC2R 0RL.

www.pearsonschools.co.uk

Text © Pearson Education Limited 2018, 2022
Edited by Pearson and Florence Production Ltd
First edition edited by Pearson, Little Grey Cells Publishing Services and Haremi Ltd
Designed and typeset by Pearson and Florence Production Ltd
First edition designed and typeset by Kamae Design
Original illustrations © Pearson Education Limited 2018, 2022
Illustrated by Laura Arias, Fran and David Brylewski, Diago Diaz, Nigel Dobbyn, Virginia
Fontanabona and Nadene Naude at Beehive Illustration; Emily Skinner at Graham-Cameron
Illustration; Kamae; and Florence Production Ltd
Cover design by Pearson Education Ltd
Front and back cover illustrations by Diego Diaz and Nadene Naude at Beehive Illustration
Series editor: Tony Staneff; Lead author: Josh Lury
Authors (first edition): Tony Staneff, Josh Lury, Kate Henshall, Wei Huinv, Steph King,
Stephanie Kirk, Timothy Weal and Paul Wrangles
Consultants (first edition): Professor Liu Jian and Professor Zhang Dan

The rights of Tony Staneff and Josh Lury to be identified as authors of this work have been
asserted by them in accordance with the Copyright, Designs and Patents Act 1988.

This publication is protected by copyright, and permission should be obtained from the
publisher prior to any prohibited reproduction, storage in a retrieval system, or transmission
in any form or by any means, electronic, mechanical, photocopying, recording, or otherwise.
For information regarding permissions, request forms and the appropriate contacts, please
visit https://www.pearson.com/us/contact-us/permissions.html Pearson Education Limited
Rights and Permissions Department

First published 2018
This edition first published 2022

26 25 24 23
10 9 8 7 6 5 4

British Library Cataloguing in Publication Data
A catalogue record for this book is available from the British Library

ISBN 978 1 292 41948 0

Printed in the UK by Bell & Bain Ltd, Glasgow

For Power Maths online resources, go to:
www.activelearnprimary.co.uk

Note from the publisher
Pearson has robust editorial processes, including answer and fact checks, to ensure the accuracy of
the content in this publication, and every effort is made to ensure this publication is free of errors.
We are, however, only human, and occasionally errors do occur. Pearson is not liable for any
misunderstandings that arise as a result of errors in this publication, but it is our priority to ensure
that the content is accurate. If you spot an error, please do contact us at resourcescorrections@
pearson.com so we can make sure it is corrected.